THE COMPLETE RHYME TIME

Chosen by Barbara Ireson

Illustrated by Lesley Smith

A Red Fox Book
Published by Random House Children's Books
20 Vauxhall Bridge Road, London SW1V 2SA

A division of Random House UK Ltd

London Melbourne Sydney Auckland
Johannesburg and agencies throughout the world

Rhyme Time first published by Beaver Books 1977
Seventh impression 1990
Text © Barbara Ireson 1977
Illustrations © Century Hutchinson Ltd 1977

Rhyme Time 2 first published by Beaver Books 1984
Third impression 1989
Text © Barbara Ireson 1984
Illustrations © Century Hutchinson Ltd 1984

This edition specially produced for School Book Fairs by
Red Fox 1992

The right of Barbara Ireson to be identified as the
author of this work has been asserted by her in
accordance with the Copyright, Designs and Patents
Act, 1988

Printed and bound in Great Britain by
Cox & Wyman Ltd, Reading, Berkshire

ISBN 0 09 926441 2

Rhyme Time

My aim has been to make the Rhyme Time
books unusually wide collections of verses for
young children. Many were chosen for the
striking pictures they present, helping children
to build a store of imaginative experience.
Others were chosen for their strong verbal and
rhythmic patterns, to show the young child how
words can be fun as well as a means of com-
munication. Walter de la Mare, Ian Serraillier,
James Reeves, Eleanor Farjeon, John Walsh and
Spike Milligan are a few of the well-known
poets represented, but there are also plenty of
works by young poets who may not yet be
generally known, and all have contributed
rhymes that children will want to hear over and
over again.

B.I.

Rhyme Time

poems collected by Barbara Ireson

Illustrated by Lesley Smith

Contents

Acknowledgements

The author and publishers would like to thank the following people for giving permission to include in this anthology material which is their copyright. The publishers have made every effort to trace copyright holders. If we have inadvertently omitted to acknowledge anyone we should be most grateful if this could be brought to our attention for correction at the first opportunity.

George Allen & Unwin (Publishers) Ltd for an extract from 'Errantry', and for 'Oliphaunt', both from *The Adventures of Tom Bombadil* by J. R. R. Tolkien

Angus & Robertson (U.K.) Ltd for 'Walter Spaggot', 'Skinny Winny' and 'The Ugstabuggle' from *The Ombley-Gombley* by Peter Wesley-Smith

Atheneum Publishers for 'Wind Song', 'Go Wind', 'Waking' and 'Dragon Smoke' from *I Feel the Same Way* by Lilian Moore (text copyright © 1967 by Lilian Moore); 'Squirrel', 'Green', 'Weather Report' and 'Wet' from *Sam's Place* by Lilian Moore (text copyright © 1973 by Lilian Moore)

Adam and Charles Black Publishers for 'Ducky-Daddles' from *Speech Rhymes* by Winifred Kingdon-Ward; 'Creeping' by Hilda Adams from *Rhythm Rhymes*

Basil Blackwell Publisher for 'Last Song' by James Guthrie; 'The Hare', 'Have You Ever ...?' 'Here Comes a Knight' and 'Jonathan' from *Widdy-Widdy-Wurky* by Rose Fyleman

Jonathan Cape Ltd, Holt Rinehart and Winston, Publishers and The Estate of Robert Frost for 'The Last Word of a Bluebird' from *The Poetry of Robert Frost*, edited by Edward Connery Lathem (copyright 1916, © 1969 by Holt, Rinehart and Winston, copyright 1944 by Robert Frost)

Chatto & Windus for 'The Old Field' from *Rhyme Times Rhyme* by D. J. Enright; 'Dead Blackbird' from *A Song of Sunlight* by Phoebe Hesketh

William Cole for 'Oh, Who Will Wash the Tiger's Ears?' by Shel Silverstein (copyright © 1967 Shel Silverstein)

Curtis Brown Ltd, London on behalf of the Estate of A. A. Milne for 'The Young Puppy' from *The Sunnyside* by A.A. Milne

Curtis Brown Ltd, New York and Atheneum Publishers for 'A Monstrous Mouse' from *One Winter Night in August and Other Nonsense Jingles* by X. J. Kennedy (a Margaret K. McElderry Book, copyright © 1975 by X. J. Kennedy); Curtis Brown Ltd, New York and Little Brown and Company, Boston for 'Bananas and Cream' and 'Jug and Mug' from *Every Time I Climb a Tree* by David McCord (copyright © 1961, 1962, 1967 by David McCord)

Andre Deutsch Limited for 'Horrible Things' from *Seen Grandpa Lately* (1972) by Roy Fuller; 'It was Spring in the Fields and Woods', 'I'm alone in the evening', 'Two Cats', 'Hog-pig waits on a mountain', 'Have you seen the Hidebehind?', 'It was a stormy night' and 'Down the Road' from *Mind Your Own Business* (1974) by Michael Rosen

McGraw-Hill Book Company for 'Who' and 'Yellow Weed', both from *Little Raccoon and Poems from the Woods* by Lilian Moore (copyright © 1975 by Lilian Moore)

Methuen Children's Books Ltd and McClelland and Stewart Limited, Toronto for 'Furry Bear' from *Now We Are Six* and 'Happiness' from *When we Were Very Young* by A. A. Milne; Methuen Children's Books Ltd for 'Lightships' and 'Me – Pirate' from *The Golden Unicorn* by Clive Sansom

Michael Joseph for 'Moon – Come – Out' and 'In the Week when Christmas Comes' from *Silver Sand and Snow* by Eleanor Farjeon

Oxford University Press for 'Heltery-Skeltery', 'Christmas Stocking' and 'Advice to a Child' from '*The Children's Bells*' by Eleanor Farjeon; 'I Visit the Queen', 'Alone in the Grange' and 'The Dustbin Men' from *The Night of the Wild Horses* by Gregory Harrison; 'Time to go Home' and 'The Intruder' by James Reeves

Pitman Publishing Ltd for 'If only I had plenty of money' from *Songs and Marching Tunes for Children* by Paul Edmonds

Richard Rieu for 'Two People' from *Cuckoo Calling* by E. V. Rieu

Russell & Volkening, Inc. and Alfred A. Knopf, Inc., New York, for 'Eggs are laid by turkeys', 'Hello's a handy word to say' and 'Good morning when it's morning' from *Nuts to You and Nuts to Me* by Mary Ann Hoberman (copyright © 1974 by Mary Ann Hoberman)

Scott, Foresman and Company for 'Bird Talk' and 'After a Bath' from *Up the Windy Hill* by Aileen Fisher

Sidgwick & Jackson for 'Choosing Shoes 'and 'Uncle John's Pig' from *The Very Thing* by Ffrida Wolfe

Ian Serraillier for 'The Mouse in the Wainscot' (copyright © 1950), extract from 'The Hedgehog' (copyright © 1963), 'Too Polite' (copyright © 1963) and 'Peter, Peter, Pumpkin-eater' (copyright © 1946)

William Jay Smith for 'There was an old man of Toulon'

The Society of Authors as the literary representative of the Estate of Rose Fyleman for 'Witch, Witch' and 'Hen's Song'

Stainer & Bell Ltd for 'Seed Song' from *The Land of Wrong Way Round* by Christopher Rowe

Mrs A. M. Walsh for 'Skipping Song' from *The Roundabout by the Sea* by John Walsh

Mrs Iris Wise and Macmillan, London and Basingstoke for 'The Wind' and 'White Fields' from *Collected Poems* by James Stephens

World's Work Ltd and Aileen Fisher for 'The Frog's Lament' from *In the Woods, In the Meadow, In the Sky* by Aileen Fisher; World's Work Ltd and Grosset & Dunlap, Inc. for 'Skilly Oogan', 'Home from the Carnival' and 'The Friendly Cinnamon Bun' from *The Pedalling Man and Other Poems* by Russell Hoban (copyright © 1968 by Russell Hoban); World's Work Ltd and Doubleday & Company, Inc. for 'What is Red?' from *Hailstones and Halibut Bones* by Mary O'Neill (copyright © 1961 by Mary Le Duc O'Neill)

Bananas and Cream

Bananas and Cream

Bananas and cream,
Bananas and cream:
All we could say was
Bananas and cream.

We couldn't say fruit,
We couldn't say cow,
We didn't say sugar –
We don't say it now.

Bananas and cream,
Bananas and cream,
All we could shout was
Bananas and cream.

We didn't say why,
We didn't say how;
We forgot it was fruit,
We forgot the old cow;
We *never* said sugar,
We only said WOW!

Bananas and cream,
Bananas and cream;
All that we want is
Bananas and cream!

We didn't say dish,
We didn't say spoon;
We said not tomorrow,
But NOW and HOW SOON

Bananas and cream,
Bananas and cream?
We yelled for bananas,
Bananas and scream!

David McCord

The Kettle

There's a little metal kettle
That is sitting near the settle.
You will hear the tittle-tattle
Of the lid begin to rattle
When the kettle starts to boil.
What a pretty prittle-prattle
Of the kettle near the settle,
Such a merry tittle-tattle
When the lid begins to rattle
And the kettle starts to boil.

Gwynneth Thurburn

Cow

'Cow' sounds heavy.
Cow
Standing in the meadow
Chewing.
A big fur box on legs
Mooing.

Karla Kuskin

Six Times One

Is six times one a lot of fun?
Or eight times two?
Perhaps for you.
But five times three
Unhinges me,
While six and seven and eight times eight
Put me in an awful state
And four and six and nine times nine
Make me want to cry and whine
So when I get to twelve times ten
I begin to wonder when
I can take a vacation from multiplication
And go out
And start playing again.

Karla Kuskin

Robert Rowley

Robert Rowley rolled a round roll round,
A round roll Robert Rowley rolled round.
Where rolled the round roll Robert Rowley rolled round?

Anon.

What is This Here?

With my hands on my head, what is this here?
This is my THINKER, right over here.
That's what I learned in school.

With my hands on my head, what is this here?
This is my I-SEE-YOU, right over here.
Thinker, I-see-you, hinky dinky do.
That's what I learned in school.

With my hands on my head, what is this here?
This is my SNEEZE-MAKER, right over here.
Thinker, I-see-you, sneeze-maker, hinky dinky do.
That's what I learned in school.

With my hands on my head, what is this here?
This is my SOUP STRAINER, right over here.
Thinker, I-see-you, sneeze-maker, soup strainer,
   hinky dinky do.
That's what I learned in school.

With my hands on my neck, what is this here?
This is my COLLAR HOLDER, right over here.
Thinker, I-see-you, sneeze-maker, soup strainer,
   collar holder, hinky dinky do.
That's what I learned in school.

With my hands on my body, what is this here?
This is my BREAD BASKET, right over here.
Thinker, I-see-you, sneeze-maker, soup strainer,
   collar holder, bread basket, hinky dinky do.
That's what I learned in school.

With my hands on my body, what is this here?
This is my BELT HOLDER, right over here.
Thinker, I-see-you, sneeze-maker, soup strainer,
   collar holder, bread basket, belt holder,
   hinky dinky do.
That's what I learned in school.

With my hands on my legs, what is this here?
This is my KNEE CAPPER, right over here.
Thinker, I-see-you, sneeze-maker, soup strainer,
   collar holder, bread basket, belt holder, knee
   capper, hinky dinky do.
That's what I learned in school.

With my hands on my feet, what is this here?
This is my SHOE HOLDER, right over here.
Thinker, I-see-you, sneeze-maker, soup strainer,
   collar holder, bread basket, belt holder, knee
   capper, shoe holder, hinky dinky do.
That's what I learned in school.

Anon.

Jug and Mug

'Jug, aren't you fond of Mug?'
'Him I could hug,' said Jug.
'Mug, aren't you fond of Jug?'
'Him I could almost slug!'
'Humph,' said Jug with a shrug.
'When he pours, he goes *Glug*!' said Mug.
'Well, *I* don't spill on the rug,' said Jug.
'Smug old Jug,' said Mug.
'I'll fill you, Mug,' said Jug.
'*Will*, will you, Jug!' said Mug.
'Don't be ugly,' said Jug juggly.
'Big lug,' said Mug.
Glug.

David McCord

Who Am I?

As black as ink and isn't ink,
As white as milk and isn't milk,
As soft as silk and isn't silk,
And hops about like a filly-foal.

Anon.

(A magpie)

Hello's a handy word

Hello's a handy word to say
At least a hundred times a day.
Without Hello what would I do
Whenever I bumped into you?
Without Hello where would you be
Whenever you bumped into me?
Hello's a handy word to know.
Hello Hello Hello Hello.

Mary Ann Hoberman

Good morning when it's morning

Good morning when it's morning
Good night when it is night
Good evening when it's dark out
Good day when it is light
Good morning to the sunshine
Good evening to the sky
And when it's time to go away
Good-bye
Good-bye
Good-bye.

Mary Ann Hoberman

What is Red?

Red is a sunset
Blazing and bright.
Red is feeling brave
With all your might.
Red is a sunburn
Spot on your nose.
Sometimes red
Is a red, red rose.
Red squiggles out
When you cut your hand.
Red is a brick and
The sound of a band.
Red is a hotness
You get inside
When you're embarrassed
And want to hide.
Firecracker, fire-engine
Fire-flicker red –
And when you're angry
Red runs through your head.
Red is an Indian,
A valentine heart,
The trimming on
A circus cart.

Red is a lipstick,
Red is a shout,
Red is a signal
That says: 'Watch out!'
Red is a great big
Rubber ball.
Red is the giant-est
Colour of all.
Red is a show-off
No doubt about it –
But can you imagine
Living without it?

Mary O'Neil

My Dame hath a Lame Tame Crane

My Dame hath a lame tame crane
My Dame hath a crane that is lame
Pray gentle Jane,
Let my Dame's lame tame crane
Feed and come home again.

Anon.

Ten hens

Ten hens
Nine lines
Eight plates
Seven elevens
Six picks
Five hives
Four doors
Three trees
Two shoes
AND ONE GREAT BIG BUN

Barbara Ireson

A Nonsense Alphabet

A   was an ape,
Who stole some white tape
And tied up his toes
In four beautiful bows.
            a!
        Funny old Ape!

B   was a bat,
Who slept all the day
And fluttered about
When the sun went away.
            b!
        Brown little Bat!

C   was a camel,
You rode on his hump
And if you fell off,
You came down such a bump!
            c!
        What a high Camel!

D   was a dove
Who lived in a wood
With such pretty soft wings,
And so gentle and good.
            d!
        Dear little Dove!

E was an eagle
Who sat on the rocks
And looked down on the fields
And the far away flocks.
        e!
    Beautiful Eagle!

F was a fan
Made of beautiful stuff
And when it was used
It went – Puffy-puff-puff!
        f!
    Nice little Fan!

G was a gooseberry
Perfectly red;
To be made into jam
And eaten with bread.
        g!
    Gooseberry red!

H was a heron
Who stood in a stream
The length of his neck
And his legs, was extreme.
        h!
    Long-legged Heron!

I was an inkstand
Which stood on a table
With a nice pen to write with,
When we were able!
        i!
    Neat little Inkstand!

J was a jug,
So pretty and white
With fresh water in it
At morning and night.
        j!
    Nice little Jug!

K was a kingfisher,
Quickly he flew
So bright and so pretty,
Green, purple and blue.
        k!
    Kingfisher, blue!

L was a lily
So white and so sweet
To see it and smell it
Was quite a nice treat!
        l!
    Beautiful Lily!

M was a man,
Who walked round and round,
And he wore a long coat
That came down to the ground.
        m!
    Funny old Man!

N was a nut
So smooth and so brown,
And when it was ripe
It fell tumble-dum-down.
        n!
    Nice little Nut!

O   was an oyster
Who lived in his shell,
If you left him alone
He felt perfectly well.
           o!
   Open-mouthed Oyster!

P   was a polly
All red, blue and green
The most beautiful polly
That ever was seen.
           p!
      Poor little Polly!

Q   was a quill
Made into a pen,
But I do not know where
And I cannot say when.
           q!
      Nice little Quill!

R   was a rattlesnake
Rolled up so tight,
Those who saw him ran quickly
For fear he should bite.
           r!
      Rattlesnake bite!

S   was a screw
To screw down a box
And then it was fastened
Without any locks.
           s!
      Valuable Screw!

T   was a thimble
Of silver so bright
When placed on the finger
It fitted so tight!
t!
Nice little Thimble!

U   was an upper-coat
Woolly and warm
To wear over all
In the snow or the storm.
u!
What a nice Upper-coat!

V   was a veil
With a border upon it
And a riband to tie it
All round a pink bonnet.
v!
Pretty green Veil!

W   was a watch
Where in letters of gold
The hour of the day
You might always behold.
       w!
    Beautiful Watch!

X   was King Xerxes
Who wore on his head
A mighty large turban,
Green, yellow and red.
       x!
  Look at King Xerxes!

Y   was a yak
From the land of Thibet
Except his white tail
He was all black as jet.
       y!
  Look at the Yak!

Z   was a zebra,
All striped white and black,
And if he were tame
You might ride on his back.
       z!
  Pretty striped Zebra!

Edward Lear

What's in There?

What's in there?
  Gold and moncy.
Where's my share of it?
  The mouse ran away with it.
Where's the mouse?
  In her house.

Where's the house?
  In the wood.
Where's the wood?
  The fire burnt it.
Where's the fire?
  The water quenched it.

Where's the water?
  The brown bull drank it.
Where's the brown bull?
  At the back of Birnie's Hill.
Where's Birnie's Hill?
  All clad with snow.
Where's the snow?
  The sun melted it.
Where's the sun?
  High, high up in the air.

Anon.

There's a Hole in the Middle of the Sea

There's a hole, there's a hole, there's a hole in the middle of the sea.

There's a log in the hole in the middle of the sea.

There's a hole, there's a hole, there's a hole in the middle of the sea.

There's a bump on the log in the hole in the middle of the sea.

There's a hole, there's a hole, there's a hole in the middle of the sea.

There's a frog on the bump on the log in the hole in the middle
of the sea.

There's a hole, there's a hole, there's a hole in the middle of the sea.

There's a fly on the frog on the bump on the log in the hole in the
middle of the sea.

There's a hole, there's a hole, there's a hole in the middle of the sea.

There's a wing on the fly on the frog on the bump on the log in the hole in the middle of the sea.

There's a hole, there's a hole, there's a hole in the middle of the sea.

There's a flea on the wing on the fly on the frog on the bump on the log in the hole in the middle of the sea.

There's a hole, there's a hole, there's a hole in the middle of the sea.

Anon.

On the Ning Nang Nong

On the Ning Nang Nong
Where the Cows go Bong!
And the Monkeys all say Boo!
There's a Nong Nang Ning
Where the trees go Ping!
And the tea pots Jibber Jabber Joo.
On the Nong Ning Nang
All the mice go Clang!
And you just can't catch 'em when they do!
So it's Ning Nang Nong!
Cows go Bong!
Nong Nang Ning!
Trees go Ping!
Nong Ning Nang!
The mice go Clang!
What a noisy place to belong,
Is the Ning Nang Ning Nang Nong!!

Spike Milligan

The Mouse and the Fire Engines

Here is a house, a neat little place
With antimacassars and curtains of lace,
That stood in a street in Stirling.

Here is a mouse
That appeared in the house,
A neat little place
With curtains of lace
That stood in a street in Stirling.

Here is Miss Simpson who uttered a yell
As out of the house she rushed pell-mell
At the sight of the mouse
That appeared in her house,
A neat little place
With curtains of lace
That stood in a street in Stirling.

Here is a boy who sings in the choir
Running and waving and shouting 'Fire!'
When little Miss Simpson uttered a yell
As out of the house she rushed pell-mell
At the sight of the mouse
That appeared in her house,
A neat little place
With curtains of lace
That stood in a street in Stirling.

Here is a policeman on his beat,
Marching with dignity down the street,
Who met the boy who sings in the choir,
Running and waving and shouting 'Fire!'
When little Miss Simpson uttered a yell
As out of the house she rushed pell-mell
At the sight of the mouse
That appeared in her house,
A neat little place
With curtains of lace
That stood in a street in Stirling.

Here is the operator clearing the line
For somebody dialling 999;
For the dignified policeman went from his beat
To the telephone box at the end of the street
When he met the boy who sings in the choir,
Running and waving and shouting 'Fire!'
When little Miss Simpson uttered a yell
As out of the house she rushed pell-mell
At the sight of the mouse
That appeared in her house,
A neat little place
With curtains of lace
That stood in a street in Stirling.

Here are the fire engines, three or four,
Their bells are ringing, their engines roar;

For the telephone girl has cleared the line
For somebody dialling 999;
For the dignified policeman went from his beat
To the telephone box at the end of the street
When he met the boy who sings in the choir,
Running and waving and shouting 'Fire!'
When little Miss Simpson uttered a yell
As out of the house she rushed pell-mell
At the sight of the mouse
That appeared in her house,
A neat little place
With curtains of lace
That stood in a street in Stirling.

Here is Miss Simpson who, much upset,
Has a narrow escape from getting wet;
For the firemen propose
To turn on the hose,
Without pause to inquire
Whereabouts is the fire,
But Miss Simpson calls out at the very last minute
That this is *her* house and there's not a fire in it.
It's a neat little place
With curtains of lace
That stood in a street in Stirling.

Here are the firemen coiling their hose.
They jump on the engines and everyone goes,
Bicycles, cars and folk on their feet,
Even the policeman returns to his beat.
Then the boy and Miss Simpson search for the mouse,
From attic to cellar they ransack the house,
A neat little place
With curtains of lace
That stood in a street in Stirling.

Here is the magistrate frowning next day
And stating severely that someone must pay
For fire engines' petrol and firemen's wages,
And ferreting out by steps and stages
What is the name
Of the person to blame,
Wishful to find and to punish the same.
The policeman declared that he couldn't decline
To dial the number 999.
The choirboy explained how he made the mistake,
And little Miss Simpson, all of a quake,
Told of the mouse
That appeared in her house,
A neat little place
With curtains of lace
That stood in a street in Stirling.

At length the magistrate cleared his throat,
And first he said and then he wrote:
'The fire engines it seems were summoned in error,
Due to Miss Simpson's screams of terror;
So the mouse that caused them must bear the blame.
But, since no one can find and punish the same,
Stirling town council must pay the cost
And, doubtless, recover the money so lost
By raising the rates on each neat little place,
With antimacassars and curtains of lace,
That stands in the streets of Stirling.'

Wilma Horsbrugh

Weather Report

Wind Song

When the wind blows
The quiet things speak.
Some whisper, some clang,
Some creak.

Grasses swish.
Treetops sigh.
Flags slap
and snap at the sky.
Wires on poles
whistle and hum.
Ashcans roll.
Windows drum.

When the wind goes –
suddenly
then,
the quiet things
are quiet again.

Lilian Moore

It is grey out

It is grey out.
It is grey in.
In me
It is as grey as the day is grey.
The trees look sad
And I,
Not knowing why I do,
Cry.

Karla Kuskin

Dragon Smoke

Breathe and blow
white clouds
    with every puff.
It's cold today,
    cold enough
to see your breath.
Huff!
    Breathe dragon smoke
    today!

Lilian Moore

Down the Road

Down the road
we see behind wet windows
eyes up
trying to pull the clouds apart.
Before they come out again
they want to see dry islands on the paving-stones
and the drips from the bricks go warm.

We're listening to Niagara in the drains
and camping in Cape Horn under the butcher's awning.
We change guard at the tobacconist
watch petrol rainbows in the gutter.
A dog droops there
wishing he had a sou'wester on;
and like our ball hitting the chicken-wire
as he shudders his body
he makes a show of his own rain too.

Michael Rosen

The Wind

The wind stood up, and gave a shout;
He whistled on his fingers, and

Kicked the withered leaves about,
And thumped the branches with his hand,

And said he'll kill, and kill, and kill;
And so he will! And so he will!

James Stephens

Windy Nights

Rumbling in the chimneys,
   Rattling at the doors,
Round the roofs and round the roads
   The rude wind roars;
Raging through the darkness,
   Raving through the trees,
Racing off again across
   The great grey seas.

Rodney Bennett

Rain Sizes

Rain comes in various sizes.
Some rain is as small as a mist.
It tickles your face with surprises,
And tingles as if you'd been kissed.

Some rain is the size of a sprinkle
And doesn't put out all the sun.
You can see the drops sparkle and twinkle,
And a rainbow comes out when it's done.

Some rain is as big as a nickel
And comes with a crash and a hiss.
It comes down too heavy to tickle.
It's more like a splash than a kiss.

When it rains the right size and you're wrapped in
Your rainclothes, it's fun out of doors.
But run home before you get trapped in
The big rain that rattles and roars.

John Ciardi

Rain

I opened my eyes
And looked up at the rain
And it dripped in my head
And flowed into my brain
So pardon this wild crazy thing I just said
I'm just not the same since there's rain in my head.
I step very softly
I walk very slow
I can't do a hand-stand
Or I might overflow.
And all I can hear as I lie in my bed
Is the slishity-slosh of the rain in my head.

Shel Silverstein

The Rain

The rain is raining all around,
It falls on field and tree;
It rains on the umbrellas here
And on the ships at sea.

Robert Louis Stevenson

Days that the wind takes over

Days that the wind takes over
Blowing through the gardens
Blowing birds out of the street trees
Blowing cats around corners
Blowing my hair out
Blowing my heart apart
Blowing high in my head
Like the sea sound caught in a shell.
One child put her thin arms around the wind
And they went off together.
Later the wind came back
Alone.

Karla Kuskin

Thunder

I hear thunder.
I hear thunder.
Hark! Don't you?
Hark! Don't you?
Pitter-patter, raindrops,
Pitter-patter, raindrops,
I'm wet through,
So are you.

Anon.

Week of Winter Weather

On Monday icy rain poured down
and flooded drains all over town.

Tuesday's gales rent elm and ash;
dead branches came down with a crash.

On Wednesday bursts of hail and sleet:
no-one walked along our street.

Thursday stood out clear and calm
but the sun was paler than my arm.

Friday's frost that bit your ears
was cold enough to freeze your tears.

Saturday's sky was ghostly grey;
we smashed ice on the lake today.

Christmas Eve was Sunday and
snow fell like foam across the land.

Wes Magee

Who?

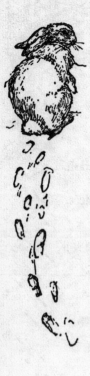

Who's been
criss-
crossing
this
fresh snow?

Well, Rabbit was here.
How did he go?
Hop–hopping.
Stopping.
Hopping away.

A deer
stood near
this tall young tree.
Took three steps.
(What did she see?)
Didn't stay.
(What did she hear?)

Fox brushed snow dust
from a bush.
Squirrel, too.
But who –
WHO
walked on TWO legs
here
today?

Lilian Moore

Go Wind

Go wind, blow
Push wind, swoosh.
  Shake things
  take things
  make things
    fly.

  Rings things
  swing things
  fling things
    high.

Go wind, blow
Push things . . . wheee.
  No, wind, no.
  Not me –
  not *me*.

Lilian Moore

Little Wind

Little wind, blow on the hill-top,
  Little wind, blow down the plain;
Little wind, blow up the sunshine,
  Little wind, blow off the rain.

Kate Greenaway

Rain

Rain on the green grass,
And rain on the tree,
And rain on the house-top,
But not upon me!

Anon.

Wet

Wet wet wet
the world of melting winter,
icicles weeping themselves away
on the eaves
little brown rivers streaming
down the road
nibbling
at the edges of the tired snow,
   all puddled mud
   not a dry place to put
   a booted foot,
everything
   dripping
   slipping
   gushing
   slushing
and listen to that brook,
rushing
like a puppy loosed from its leash.

Lilian Moore

White Fields

In the winter time we go
Walking in the fields of snow;

Where there is no grass at all;
Where the top of every wall,

Every fence, and every tree
Is as white as white can be.

Pointing out the way we came –
Every one of them the same –

All across the fields there be
Prints in silver filligree;

And our mothers always know,
By the footprints in the snow,

Where it is the children go.

James Stephens

Weather Report

Pinging rain
stinging sleet
tonight.

Frost at dawn,
bright
sun in the morning.

Ice-bearing trees,
a glass
orchard,
blinking
sunwinking.

A noonwind will
pass,
harvesting the brittle crop,
crashing
clinking.

Lilian Moore

Time to Get Up

Waking

My secret way of waking
is like a place
to hide.
I'm very still,
my eyes are shut.
They all think I am sleeping
but
I'm wide awake inside.

They all think I am sleeping
but
I'm wiggling my toes.
I feel sun-fingers
on my cheek.
I hear voices whisper-speak.
I squeeze my eyes
to keep them shut
so they will think I'm sleeping
BUT
I'm really wide awake inside
– and no one knows!

Lilian Moore

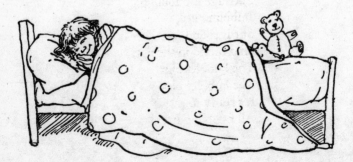

Time to Get Up

A bird who had a yellow bill
Landed on my window sill,
Winked his shining eye and said,
'Time to get up, Sleepy Head!'

Robert Louis Stevenson

Porridge is bubbling

Porridge is bubbling,
Bubbling hot,
Stir it round
And round in the pot.
The bubbles plip!
The bubbles plop!
It's ready to eat
All bubbling hot.

Anon.

The Dustbin Men

The older ones have gone to school,
My breakfast's on the plate,
But I can't leave the window-pane,
I might be just too late.

I've heard the clatter down the street,
I know they're creeping near,
The team of gruff-voiced, burly men
Who keep our dustbins clear.

And I must watch and see them clang
The dustbins on the road,
And stand in pairs to heave up high
The double-handled load.

Yes, there they come, the lorry growls
And grinds in bottom gear;
The dustman knees the garden gate
As, high up by his ear,
Firmly he balances the bin,
Head tilted to one side;
The great mouth of the rubbish cart
Is yawning very wide;
To me the mouth looks like a beast's
A dragon's hungry jaws
That snap the refuse out of sight
Behind those sliding doors.

The lorry-dragon every day
Is in a ravenous mood,
And cardboard boxes, bottles, jars
Are all part of his food.

He gobbles up old magazines,
Saucepans and broken jugs
Pieces of red linoleum,
And dirty, tufted rugs.

He crunches shattered pictures,
Old bicycles and tyres,
A bird-cage with its seed-tray,
Its bell and rusty wires;

And fractured clocks and mirrors,
A rocking-chair and broom,
A mattress and an iron bed;
Where does he find the room?

And like a dragon sated,
His great maw crammed quite tight,
He lifts his head and swallows
His breakfast out of sight.

What would the careless people
Who clutter up the street
Do without hungry dragons
To keep our houses neat?

Gregory Harrison

Summer Goes

Summer goes, summer goes
Like the sand between my toes
When the waves go out.
That's how summer pulls away,
Leaves me standing here today,
Waiting for the school bus.

Summer brought, summer brought
All the frogs that I have caught,
Frogging at the pond,
Hot dogs, flowers, shells and rocks,
Postcards in my postcard box –
Places far away.

Summer took, summer took
All the lessons in my book,
Blew them far away.
I forgot the things I knew –
Arithmetic and spelling too,
Never thought about them.

Summer's gone, summer's gone –
Fall and winter coming on,
Frosty in the morning.
Here's the school bus right on time.
I'm not really sad that I'm
Going back to school.

Russell Hoban

Betty and I

Betty my sister and I fell out,
And what do you think it was all about?
She loved coffee and I loved tea,
And that was the reason we could not agree.

Anon.

As I was going along

As I was going along, long, long,
A-singing a comical song, song, song,
The lane that I went was so long, long, long,
And the song that I sang was so long, long, long,
That the words and the music went wrong, wrong, wrong,
As I went singing along!

Anon.

At the Seaside

When I was down beside the sea
A wooden spade they gave to me
  To dig the sandy shore.

My holes were empty like a cup.
In every hole the sea came up
  Till it could come no more.

Robert Louis Stevenson

Skipping Song

When bread-and-cheese
  on hawthorn trees
makes buds of tiny green;
When big dogs chase
  around, and little
dogs run in between;
When shouts and songs
  and arguments
are heard on every lip;
Then is the time
  when all true-minded
children want to skip.
To-skip-skip-skip-skip-skip-skip-skip.
The-time-when-all-the-children-want-to-skip.

When days grow long,
  and sister Jean
with Bobby Bates goes walking;
  When steps are warm
  for sitting on,
and pavements dry for chalking;
When last year's summer
  frocks come out,
and thrill with summer hope;
Then is the time
  to search the house
and find a piece of rope.
It's-the-time-time-time-time-time-time-time-
to-search-the-house-and-find-a-piece-of-rope.

There's skipping ropes
   so thin and light
it's hard to twirl them round;
There's hairy ropes with
   knots, and heavy
ropes that slap the ground;
And bits of plastic
   washing line
are there among the rest;
But of all the ropes
   the rope with painted
handles is the best.
It's-the-best-best-best-best-best-best-best.
The rope with painted handles is the best –
THAT'S MINE.

John Walsh

Whip Top

Whip top! Whip top!
Turn about and never stop!
Monday's top will spin away,
Tuesday's top will sing all day,
Wednesday's top is never slow,
Thursday's top to sleep will go,
Friday's top will dance about,
Saturday's top will tire you out!
Whip top! Whip top!
Spin around and never stop!

Anon.

Me, myself, and I

Me, myself, and I –
We went to the kitchen and ate a pie.
Then my mother she came in
And chased us out with a rolling pin.

Anon.

The Tidy Child

My little broom is made of twigs
Tied round and round with bright green string,
With it, on windy autumn days
   I do my tidying.

I sweep and sweep the yellow leaves
That tumble from our great oak tree,
And when I sit down for a rest
   They tumble on to me.

Barbara Baker

Pancake Day

Mummy made pancakes on Tuesday,
She tossed them in the air,
One fell on the table,
Two fell on the chair,
One fell on the cooker
And one fell in the grate,
But, lucky for me,
I had three
Because they fell on my plate.

Shaun Fountain

Drinking Fountain

When I climb up
   To get a drink,
It doesn't work
   The way you'd think.

I turn it up.
   The water goes
And hits me right
   Upon the nose.

I turn it down
   To make it small
And don't get any
   Drink at all.

Marchette Chute

The Old Field

The old field is sad
Now the children have gone home.
They have played with him all afternoon,
Kicking the ball to him, and him
Kicking it back.

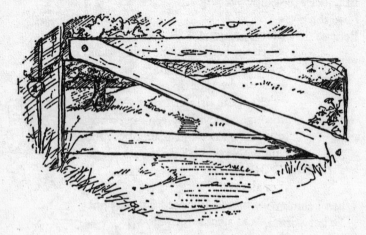

But now it is growing cold and dark.
He thinks of their warm breath, and their
Feet like little hot-water bottles.
A bit rough, some of them, but still . . .

And now, he thinks, there's not even a dog
To tickle me.
The gates are locked.
The birds don't like this nasty sneaking wind,
And nor does he.

D. J. Enright

I'm alone in the evening

I'm alone in the evening
when the family sits
reading and sleeping,
and I watch the fire in close
to see flame goblins
wriggling out of their caves
for the evening

Later I'm alone
when the bath has gone cold around me
and I have put my foot
beneath the cold tap
where it can dribble
through valleys between my toes
out across the white plain of my foot
and bibble bibble into the sea

I'm alone
when mum's switched out the light
my head against the pillow
listening to ca thump ca thump
in the middle of my ears.
It's my heart.

Michael Rosen

After a Bath

After my bath
I try, try, try
to wipe myself
till I'm dry, dry, dry.

Hands to wipe
and fingers and toes
and two wet legs
and a shiny nose.

Just think how much
less time I'd take
if I were a dog
and could shake, shake, shake.

Aileen Fisher

The Falling Star

I saw a star slide down the sky,
Blinding the north as it went by,
Too lovely to be bought or sold,
Too burning and too quick to hold,
Good only to make wishes on
And then forever to be gone.

Sara Teasdale

February Twilight

I stood beside a hill
  Smooth with new-laid snow,
A single star looked out
  From the cold evening glow.

There was no other creature
  That saw what I could see –
I stood and watched the evening star
  As long as it watched me.

                    Sara Teasdale

Last Song

To the Sun
Who has shone
  All day,
To the Moon
Who has gone
  Away,
To the milk-white
Silk-white,
Lily-white Star,
A fond good-night
Wherever you are.

    James Guthrie

Roll Over

There were ten in the bed
And the little one said:
  'Roll over! Roll over!'
So they all rolled over,
And one fell out.

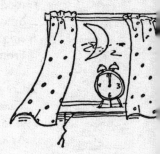

There were nine in the bed
And the little one said:
  'Roll over! Roll over!'
So they all rolled over,
And one fell out.

There were eight in the bed
And the little one said:
  'Roll over! Roll over!'
So they all rolled over
And one fell out.

There were seven in the bed
And the little one said:
  'Roll over! Roll over!'
So they all rolled over,
And one fell out.

There were six in the bed
And the little one said:
  'Roll over! Roll over!'
So they all rolled over,
And one fell out.

There were five in the bed
And the little one said:
  'Roll over! Roll over!'
So they all rolled over,
And one fell out.

There were four in the bed
And the little one said:
  'Roll over! Roll over!'
So they all rolled over,
And one fell out.

There were three in the bed
And the little one said:
  'Roll over! Roll over!'
So they all rolled over,
And one fell out.

There were two in the bed
And the little one said:
  'Roll over! Roll over!'
So they all rolled over,
And one fell out.

There was one in the bed
And the little one said:
  'Roll over! Roll over!'
So HE rolled over,
And HE fell out.

So there was the bed –
And no one said:
  'Roll over! Roll over!'

Anon.

Night-lights

There is no need to light a night-light
On a light night like tonight;
For a night-light's light's a slight light
When the moonlight's white and bright.

Anon.

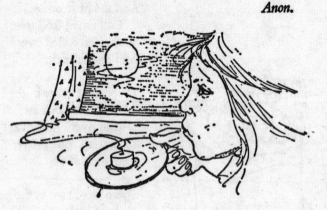

Moon – Come – Out

Moon – Come – Out
And Sun – Go – In,
Here's a soft blanket
To cuddle your chin.

Moon – Go – In
And Sun – Come – Out,
Throw off the blanket
And bustle about.

Eleanor Farjeon

What the Leaves Said

The Leaves are Green

The leaves are green
The nuts are brown,
They hang so high
They will not come down.

Leave them alone
Till frosty weather,
Then they will all
Come down together.

Anon.

Autumn

Yellow the bracken,
Golden the sheaves,
Rosy the apples,
Crimson the leaves;
Mist on the hillside,
Clouds grey and white.
Autumn, good morning!
Summer, good night.

Florence Hoatson

What the Leaves Said

The leaves said, 'It's spring;
And here are we,
Opening and stretching on every tree.'

The leaves said, 'It's summer;
Each bird has a nest;
We make the shadow
Where they can rest.'

The leaves said, 'It's autumn;
Aren't we all gay?'
Scarlet and golden
And russet were they.

The leaves said, 'It's winter;
Weary are we.'
So they lay down and slept
Under the tree.

Anon.

A little bit of blowing

A little bit of blowing,
  A little bit of snow,
A little bit of growing,
  And the crocuses will show;
On every twig that's lonely
  A new green leaf will spring;
On every patient tree-top
  A thrush will perch and sing.

Anon.

In the fields

One day I saw a big brown cow
Raise her head and chew,
I said 'Good morning, Mrs Cow,'
But all she said was 'Moo!'

One day I saw a woolly lamb,
I followed it quite far,
I said 'Good morning, little lamb,'
But all it said was 'Baa!'

One day I saw a dappled horse
Cropping in the hay,
I said 'Good morning, Mr Horse,'
But all he said was 'Neigh!'

Anon.

On the Farm

I went to visit a farm one day
And saw a pig across the way.
Now what do you think I heard it say?

OINK, OINK, OINK.

I went to visit a farm one day
And saw a sheep across the way.
Now what do you think I heard it say?

BAA, BAA, BAA.

I went to visit a farm one day
And saw a cow across the way.
Now what do you think I heard it say?

MOO, MOO, MOO.

Anon.

Earth-worm

Do
you
squirm
when
you
see
an earth-worm?
I never
do squirm
because I think
a big fat worm
is really rather clever
the way it can shrink
and go
so small
without
a sound
into the ground.
And then
what about
all
that
work it does
and no oxygen
or miner's hat?
Marvellous
you have to admit,
even if you don't like fat

pink worms a bit,
how with that
thin
slippery skin
it makes its way
day after day
through the soil,
such honest toil.
And don't forget
the dirt
it eats, I bet
you wouldn't like to come out
at night to squirt
it all over the place
with no eyes in your face:
I doubt
too if you know
an earth-worm is deaf, but
it can hear YOU go
to and fro
even if you cut
it in half,
do not laugh
or squirm
again
when
you
suddenly
see
a worm.

Leonard Clark

Yellow Weed

How did you get here,
weed?
Who brought your seed?

Did it lift
on the wind and
sail
and drift
from a far and yellow
field?

Was your seed a
burr,
a sticky burr that
clung to a
fox's
furry tail?

Did it fly with a
bird
who liked to feed
on the tasty
seed
of the yellow
weed?
How did you come?

Lilian Moore

74

Seed Song

This is a story about a seed
Lying in the ground
Which slept right through the wintertime
Till Springtime came around.

When all at once the sunshine came
And drops of gentle rain,
The ground became much warmer
And the seed woke up again.

Then from the seed there grew a root
Which wriggled in the ground;
Root from the seed,
That wonderful seed
Way down in the ground.

Then from the root there came a shoot
Which came up for some air;
Shoot from the root,
Root from the seed
That wonderful seed
Way down in the ground.

Then from the shoot there came a leaf
When the sun began to shine;
Leaf from the shoot,
Shoot from the root,
Root from the seed,
That wonderful seed
Way down in the ground.

Then from the leaf there came a plant
Watered by the roots;
Plant from the leaf,
Leaf from the shoot,
Shoot from the root,
Root from the seed,
That wonderful seed
Way down in the ground.

Then from the plant there came a bud
As summer came around;
Bud from the plant,
Plant from the leaf,
Leaf from the shoot,
Shoot from the root,

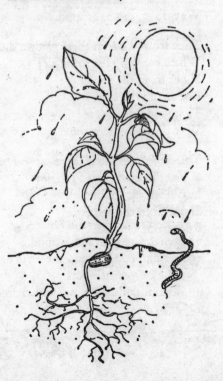

Root from the seed,
That wonderful seed
Way down in the ground.

Then from the bud there grew a flower
To greet the summer sun;
Flower from the bud,
Bud from the plant,
Plant from the leaf,
Leaf from the shoot,
Shoot from the root,
Root from the seed,
That wonderful seed
Way down in the ground.

But when at last the Autumn came
And leaves fell all around,
A new seed ripened in the flower
And then dropped to the ground.
The seed slipped back into the earth
Washed by the gentle rain
And slept right through the wintertime
Till Spring came around again.

Christopher Rowe

The Hills

Sometimes I think the hills
That loom across the harbour
Lie there like sleeping dragons,
Crouched one above another,
With trees for tufts of fur
Growing all up and down
The ridges and humps of their backs,
And orange cliffs for claws
Dipped in the sea below.
Sometimes a wisp of smoke
Rises out of the hollows,
As if in their dragon sleep
They dreamed of strange old battles.

What if the hills should stir
Some day and stretch themselves,
Shake off the clinging trees
And all the clustered houses?

Rachel Field

It was Spring in the Fields

It was spring in the fields and woods
the leaves in the hedges shook in the wind
as a crow stood quite still on a white horse's back.
He was looking at the grass about him
and the trees at the edge of the paddock
when all of a sudden he said to the horse beneath his feet:
Do you see how green everything is today?
and the horse said:
well to tell you the truth – no, I don't.
everything looks pink to me
you see my eyes are pink . . . he stopped.
the crow spoke again:
Oh. I'm sorry.
But how do you know that everything you see is pink
when it's the only colour you've ever seen?
The horse sat thinking about that for a while
and then said:
well of course it's quite true what you say.
In fact I was only guessing.
But you see – when I was born,
everybody pointed at me and said: look at him –
his eyes are pink. So I thought everything I saw
was pink. It seemed a sensible thing to do at the time
The crow shook his head slowly to and fro
breathed in deeply and sympathetically
and flew off to make his nest in the clear green sky.

Michael Rosen

I know a little pussy

I know a little pussy,
Her coat is silver grey;
She lives down in the meadow,
Not very far away.
Although she is a pussy,
She'll never be a cat,
For she's a pussy willow –
Now what do you think of that?

Anon.

In the Wood

Cold winter's in the wood,
  I saw him pass
Crinkling up fallen leaves
  Along the grass.

Bleak winter's in the wood,
  The birds have flown
Leaving the naked trees
  Shivering alone.

King Winter's in the wood,
  I saw him go
Crowned with a coronet
  Of crystal snow.

Eileen Mathias

The Intruder

Two-boots in the forest walks,
Pushing through the bracken stalks.

Vanishing like a puff of smoke,
Nimbletail flies up the oak.

Longears helter-skelter shoots
Into his house among the roots.

At work upon the highest bark,
Tapperbill knocks off to hark.

Painted-wings through sun and shade
Flounces off along the glade.

Not a creature lingers by,
When clumping Two-boots comes to pry.

James Reeves

Three Little Girls

Three little girls were sitting on a rail,
    Sitting on a rail,
    Sitting on a rail;
Three little girls were sitting on a rail,
    On a fine hot day in September.

What did they talk about that fine day,
    That fine day,
    That fine day?
What did they talk about that fine day,
    That fine hot day in September?

The crows and the corn they talked about,
    Talked about,
    Talked about;
But nobody knows what was said by the crows,
    On that fine hot day in September.

Kate Greenaway

If I were an apple

If I were an apple
And grew upon a tree,
I think I'd fall down
On a good boy like me.
I wouldn't stay there
Giving nobody joy;
I'd fall down at once
And say, 'Eat me, my boy.'

Anon.

Time to go Home

Time to go home!
  Says the great steeple clock.
Time to go home!
  Says the gold weathercock.
Down sinks the sun
  In the valley to sleep;
Lost are the orchards
  In blue shadows deep.
Soft falls the dew
  On cornfield and grass;
Through the dark trees
  The evening airs pass:
Time to go home,
  They murmur and say;
Birds to their homes
  Have all flown away.
Nothing shines now
  But the gold weathercock.
Time to go home!
  Says the great steeple clock.

James Reeves

At Night

The grey owl hunts when the moon is bright,
He hunts and he hoots all through the night.
The black mole digs when the moon is strong,
He scrabbles with his sharp paws all night long.
And when the moon has gone and the sky is black,
Creeping through the woods comes old Poacher Jack.

Barbara Ireson

Things to Remember

The buttercups in May,
The wild rose on the spray,
The poppy in the hay,

The primrose in the dell,
The freckled foxglove bell,
The honeysuckle's smell

Are things I would remember
When cheerless, raw November
Makes room for dark December.

James Reeves

Bring on the Clowns

Please to Remember

Here am I,
A poor old Guy:
Legs in a bonfire,
Head in the sky;

Shoeless my toes,
Wild stars behind,
Smoke in my nose,
And my eye-peeps blind;

Old hat, old straw –
In this disgrace;
While the wildfire gleams
On a mask for face.

Ay, all I am made of
Only trash is;
And soon – soon,
Will be dust and ashes.

Walter de la Mare

The Foolish Man

I knew a man who always wore
A saucepan on his head.
I asked him what he did it for –
'I don't know why,' he said.
'It always makes my ears so sore;
I am a foolish man.
I should have left it off before
And worn a frying pan.'

Christopher Chamberlain

The Cobbler

Walking through the town one day,
I peeped in a window over the way;
And putting his needle through and through,
There sat the cobbler making a shoe.
For the world, he cares never the whisk of a broom,
All he wants is elbow room.
  Rap-a-tap-tap, tick-a-tack-too –
  That is the way to make a shoe.

Anon.

Here Comes a Knight

Here comes a knight a-riding,
To the castle he has come;
The Lady Anne puts out her head;
My Lord is not at home.

There's no one but the children
And chickens in the pen;
The knight upon his charger
He says to Lady Anne:

And are the children naughty,
Or are the children good?
Oh very bad indeed, says she,
They won't do as they should.

Says he: then I'll not have them,
No use are they to me –
He turns him to the rightabout
And home again rides he.

Rose Fyleman

Peter, Peter, Pumpkin-Eater

Mrs Piper, tiny mite,
Had a giant's appetite;
She, as short as winter grass is,
Ate enough for twenty horses.
No, not even Humpty-Dumpty
Had so stretch-able a tumpty.
She ate so much when food was cheap
There wasn't any time to sleep;
When food was dear she slept all day
Or else, for lack, she pined away.
Peter, ere she'd vanished quite,
Found a pumpkin for his wife
Growing in a field alone.
He hollowed it into a home,
With door and window, leafy shutters,
Straw for pipes (in half for gutters).
Here they lived, whatever weather,
Long and happily together.
Fog or sunshine, storm or drizzle,
Peter sang while Mrs nibbled.
She never ate the pumpkin through –
The more she ate the more it grew.
Now, to end with, here's the song
That Peter sang – it isn't long:

Peter, Peter, Pumpkin-eater,
Had a wife and couldn't keep her.
He put her in a pumpkin shell
And there he kept her very well.

Ian Serraillier

Have you ever . . . ?

Have you ever heard
Of the wiggle-waggle waggon
With greedy Gregory sitting on the box?

Nobody can beat
What Gregory can eat.

A cow and a calf,
A horse and a half,
An ox and a steer,
Seven casks of beer,
Seventeen hares,
A shipload of pears,
A churchful of sheep . . .
And even then Gregory's so hungry he can't sleep!

Rose Fyleman

Two People

Two people live in Rosamund,
　And one is very nice;
The other is devoted
　To every kind of vice –

To walking where the puddles are,
　And eating far too quick,
And saying words she shouldn't know,
　And wanting spoons to lick.

Two people live in Rosamund,
　And one (I say it twice)
Is very nice *and* very good:
　The other's only nice.

E. V. Rieu

Jonathan

Jonathan Gee
Went out with his cow
He climbed up a tree
And sat on a bough.
He sat on a bough
And it broke in half,
And John's old cow
Did nothing but laugh.

Rose Fyleman

Alone in the Grange

Strange,
Strange,
Is the little old man
Who lives in the Grange.
Old,
Old;
And they say that he keeps
A box full of gold.
Bowed,
Bowed,
Is his thin little back
That once was so proud.
Soft,
Soft,
Are his steps as he climbs
The stairs to the loft.
Black,
Black,
Is the old shuttered house.
Does he sleep on a sack?

They say he does magic,
That he can cast spells,
That he prowls round the garden
Listening for bells;
That he watches for strangers,
Hates every soul,
And peers with his dark eye
Through the keyhole.

I wonder, I wonder,
As I lie in my bed,
Whether he sleeps with his hat on his head?
Is he really magician
With altar of stone
Or a lonely old gentleman
Left on his own?

Gregory Harrison

The Old Wives

Two old wives sat a-talking,
A-talking, a-talking, a-talking;
Two old wives sat a-talking
About the wind and weather –
Till their two old heads fell a-nodding,
A-nodding, a-nodding, a-nodding,
Till their two old heads fell a-nodding,
Their two old heads together.

Anon.

Proud Janey

Look at Janey coming down the street
THUMP! go the clogs upon her feet.
O, thumpety, thumpety, thump!

Look at the hat she wears on her head,
Better with a plant pot there instead.
O, thumpety, thumpety, thump!

Look at her shawl without a doubt,
It must be a dish cloth inside out.
O, thumpety, thumpety, thump!

Look at the way she walks along,
Just like a duck with its toes turned wrong.
O, thumpety, thumpety, THUMP!

Anon.

I had a little brother

I had a little brother
His name was Tiny Tim
I put him in the bathtub
To teach him how to swim
He drank up all the water
He ate up all the soap
He died last night
With a bubble in his throat
In came the doctor
In came the nurse
In came the lady
With the alligator purse
Out went the doctor
Out went the nurse
Out went the lady
With the alligator purse.

Anon.

My Sister Laura

My sister Laura's bigger than me
And lifts me up quite easily.
I can't lift her, I've tried and tried;
She must have something heavy inside.

Spike Milligan

Old John Muddlecombe

Old John Muddlecombe lost his cap,
He couldn't find it anywhere, the poor old chap.
He walked down the High Street, and everybody said,
'Silly John Muddlecombe, you've got it on your head!'

Anon.

Maggie

There was a small maiden named Maggie,
Whose dog was enormous and shaggy;
   The front end of him
   Looked vicious and grim –
But the tail end was friendly and waggy.

Anon.

There Was an Old Man of Toulon

There was an Old Man of Toulon
Who never had anything on.
   When they said: 'Wear some clothes!'
   He inquired: 'What are those?'
So they chased that man out of Toulon.

William Jay Smith

Horrible Things

'What's the horriblest thing you've seen?'
Said Nell to Jean.

'Some grey-coloured, trodden-on plasticine;
On a plate, a left-over cold baked bean;
A cloak-room ticket numbered thirteen;
A slice of meat without any lean;
The smile of a spiteful fairy-tale queen;
A thing in the sea like a brown submarine;
A cheese fur-coated in brilliant green;
A bluebottle perched on a piece of sardine.
What's the horriblest thing *you've* seen?'
Said Jean to Nell.

'Your face, as you tell
Of all the horriblest things you've seen.'

Roy Fuller

Walter Spaggot

Walter Spaggot, strange old man,
Does things wrong-ways-round,
Like back-to-front or in-side-out,
Or even up-side-down.

He puffs his pipe inside his ear,
Has glasses for his mouth,
And if he wants to travel North
Walks backwards to the South.

He comes from where he never is
And goes to where he's been,
He scrubs his shirt in the bath-tub
And baths in his washing-machine.

Walter Spaggot, strange old man,
Does things wrong-ways-round,
Like back-to-front or in-side-out,
Or even up-side-down.

(Funny old man.)

Peter Wesley-Smith

Skinny Winny

Skinny Winny,
Silly ninny,
Took a bath.

Pulled the plug.

Glug glug glug.

Question:
What do you think
happened to
Skinny Winny?

Peter Wesley-Smith

Too Polite

Broad met Stout
At the gate, and each
Was too polite to brush past.
'After you!' said Broad.
'After you!' said Stout.
They got in a dither
And went through together
And both
    stuck
      fast.

Ian Serraillier

The Land of the Bumbley Boo

In the Land of the Bumbley Boo
The people are red white and blue,
They never blow noses,
Or ever wear closes;
What a sensible thing to do!

In the Land of the Bumbley Boo
You can buy Lemon pie at the Zoo;
They give away Foxes
In little Pink Boxes
And Bottles of Dandelion Stew.

In the Land of the Bumbley Boo
You never see a Gnu,
But thousands of cats
Wearing trousers and hats
Made of Pumpkins and Pelican Glue!

Oh, the Bumbley Boo! the Bumbley Boo!
That's the place for me and you!
So hurry! Let's run!
The train leaves at one!
For the Land of the Bumbley Boo!
The wonderful Bumbley Boo–Boo–Boo!
The Wonderful Bumbley BOO!!!

Spike Milligan

The Plug-Hole Man

I know you're down there, Plug-hole Man,
  In the dark so utter,
For when I let the water out
  I hear you gasp and splutter.

And though I peer and peek and pry
  I've never seen you yet:
(I know you're down there, Plug-hole Man
  In your home so wet).

But you will not be there for long
  For I've a *plan*, you see;
I'm going to catch you, Plug-hole Man,
  And Christian's helping me.

We'll fill the bath with water hot,
  Then give the plug a heave,
And rush down to the outside drain –
  And *catch* you as you leave!

Carey Blyton

Night Starvation or The Biter Bit

At night, my Uncle Rufus
(Or so I've heard it said)
Would put his teeth into a glass
Of water by his bed.

At three o'clock one morning
He woke up with a cough,
And as he reached out for his teeth –
They bit his hand right off.

Carey Blyton

Witch, Witch

'Witch, witch, where do you fly?' . . .
'Under the clouds and over the sky.'

'Witch, witch, what do you eat?' . . .
'Little black apples from Hurricane Street.'

'Witch, witch, what do you drink?' . . .
'Vinegar, blacking and good red ink.'

'Witch, witch, where do you sleep?' . . .
'Up in the clouds where pillows are cheap.'

Rose Fyleman

Skilly Oogan

Skilly Oogan's no one you can see,
And no one else can be his friend but me,
Skilly lives where swallows live, away up high
Beneath the topmost eaves against the sky.
When all the world's asleep on moonlit nights
Up on our roof he flies his cobweb kites.
He has an acorn boat that, when it rains,
He sails in gutters, even down the drains.
Sometimes he hides in letters that I write –
Snug in the envelope and out of sight,
On six-cent stamps he travels in all weathers
And with the midnight owl returns on silent feathers.
In summer time he rides the dragonflies
Above the pond, and looks in bullfrogs' eyes
For his reflection when he combs his hair.
And sometimes when I want him he's not there;
But mostly Skilly Oogan's where I think he'll be,
And no one even knows his name but me.

Russell Hoban

Bring on the Clowns

Bring on the clowns!
Bring on the clowns!
Clowns wearing knickers
and clowns
wearing gowns.

Tall clowns and short clowns and skinny and fat,
a flat-footed clown with a jumping-jack hat.
A clown walking under a portable shower,
getting all wet just to water a flower.
A barefoot buffoon with balloons on his toes,
a clown with a polka-dot musical nose.
Clowns wearing teapots and clowns sporting plumes,
a clown with a tail made of brushes and brooms.

A balancing clown on a wobbly wheel,
seventeen clowns in an automobile.
Two jesters on pogo sticks dressed up in kilts,
pursuing a prankster escaping on stilts.
A sad-looking clown with a face like a tramp,
a clown with his stomach lit up like a lamp.
How quickly a clown can coax smiles out of frowns!
Make way for the merriment . . . bring on the clowns!

Jack Prelutsky

The famous Human Cannonball

The famous human cannonball
stands at the cannon's side.
He's very round and very small
and very dignified.

He bows to the east, he bows to the west,
he bows to the north and south,
then proudly puffing up his chest
he steps to the cannon's mouth.

The famous human cannonball
is ready to begin.
His helpers hoist him at his call
and gently stuff him in.
The air is filled with 'ahh's' and 'ohh's'
preparing for the thrill,
but when his helpers light the fuse
the audience is still.

Then in the hushed and darkened hall
the mighty cannon roars,
the famous human cannonball
shoots out and swiftly soars.

Higher and higher the cannonball flies
in a brilliant aerial burst
and catapulting through the skies
he lands in the net – feet first.

Jack Prelutsky

The Man on the Flying Trapeze

Sporting and capering high in the breeze,
cavorting about from trapeze to trapeze
is an aerial acrobat, slim as a ribbon,
as daring and free as a tree-swinging gibbon.

He hangs by his fingers, his toes and his knees,
he dangles and dips with astonishing ease,
then springs into space as though racing on wings,
gliding between his precarious swings.

He cheerfully executes perilous plunges,
dangerous dives, unforgettable lunges,
delicate scoops and spectacular swoops,
breathtaking triple flips, hazardous loops.

Then this midair magician with nerves made of steel
somersaults, catches and hangs by one heel.
As the audience roars for the king of trapezes
he takes out his handkerchief, waves it . . . and sneezes.

Balances above us, the high wire king
skips with a swivel, a sway and a swing.
He dances, he prances, he leaps through the air,
then hangs by his teeth while he's combing his hair.
He seems not to notice the perilous height
as he stands on his left hand and waves with his right.

Jack Prelutsky

Happiness

John had
Great Big
Waterproof
Boots on;
John had a
Great Big
Waterproof
Hat;

John had a
Great Big
Waterproof
Mackintosh –
And that
(Said John)
Is
That.

A. A. Milne

Where Have You Been?

Riding in the Rain

The rain comes pittering, pattering down,
  Plipperty, plipperty, plop!
The farmer drives his horse to town,
  Clipperty, clipperty, clop!
The rain comes pattering,
  The horse goes clattering,
    Clipperty, plipperty, plop!

Anon.

Sampan

Waves lap lap
Fish fins clap clap
Brown sails flap flap
Chop-sticks tap tap;

Up and down the long green river,
Oh hey, oh hey, lanterns quiver,
Willow branches brush the river,
Oh hey, oh hey, lanterns quiver.

Chop-sticks tap tap
Brown sails flap flap
Fish fins clap clap
Waves lap lap.

Anon.

Wagons, Trucks and Vans

This train is carrying passengers,
It's pulling ten coaches today
And when they get to Manchester
One coach will be taken away.

This train is carrying letters,
It's pulling nine mail vans today
And when they get to Birmingham
One van will be taken away.

This train is carrying coal dust,
It's pulling eight trucks today
And when they get to Canterbury
One truck will be taken away.

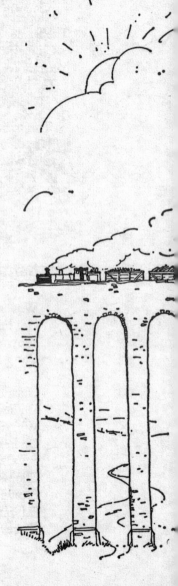

This train is carrying boxes,
It's pulling seven freight cars today
And when they get to Beverley
One car will be taken away.

This train is carrying people,
It's pulling six sleepers today
And when they get to Nottingham
One sleeper is taken away.

This train is carrying soldiers,
It's pulling five transports today
And when they get to Harrogate
One transport is taken away.

This train is carrying motor cars,
It's pulling four bogies today
And when they get to Leamington
One bogie is taken away.

This train is carrying parcels,
It's pulling three guard's vans today
And when they get to Inverness
One van will be taken away.

This train is carrying animals,
It's pulling two wagons today
And when they get to Scarborough
One truck will be taken away.

This train is carrying Her Majesty,
It's pulling the Royal Coach today
And when it gets to Edinburgh
THAT coach will be taken away.

Barbara Ireson

from Errantry

There was a merry passenger,
a messenger, a mariner:
he built a gilded gondola
to wander in, and had in her
a load of yellow oranges
and porridge for his provender;
he perfumed her with marjoram
and cardamom and lavender.

J. R. R. Tolkien

Hannibal

Hannibal crossed the Alps,
Hannibal crossed the Alps;
  With his black men,
  His brown men,
  His countrymen,
  His townmen,
With his Gauls and his Spaniards, his horses and elephants,
Hannibal crossed the Alps.

Hannibal crossed the Alps,
Hannibal crossed the Alps;
  For his bow-men,
  His spear-men,
  His front-men,
  His rear-men,
His Gauls and his Spaniards, his horses and elephants,
Wanted the Roman scalps!

And that's why
Hannibal, Hannibal, Hannibal,
Hannibal crossed the Alps.

Eleanor Farjeon

Anna Maria

Anna Maria she sat on the fire;
The fire was too hot, she sat on the pot;
The pot was too round, she sat on the ground;
The ground was too flat, she sat on the cat;
The cat ran away with Maria on her back.

Anon.

A Row of Red Coaches

A row of red coaches
Standing in a yard,
All summer long they've been
Working very hard:
Driving up the promenade,
Driving to the pier,
But now the visitors have gone
The quiet months are here.

Barbara Ireson

Down the Stream the Swans all Glide

Down the stream the swans all glide;
It's quite the cheapest way to ride.
Their legs get wet,
Their tummies wetter:
I think after all
The bus is better.

Spike Milligan

Skipping Song

The High Skip,
The Sly Skip,
The Skip like a Feather,
The Long Skip,
The Strong Skip,
And the Skip All Together!
The Slow Skip,
The Toe Skip,
The Skip Double-Double –
The Fast Skip,
The Last Skip,
And the Skip Against Trouble!

Anon.

The Blacksmith

A-hippity, hippity hop, heigh-ho!
Away to the blacksmith's shop we go.

If you've a pony
That's lost a shoe,
You can get her another
All shining and new –

A-hippity, hippity hop!

Anon.

I Visit the Queen

Ferdinand, Ferdinand,
Where have you been?
I've been up to London to look at the queen.
I've been with two horses,
A black and a grey;
They ate fifteen bundles
Of sweet-smelling hay.
At Buckingham Palace I stopped at the gate
And explained to the sentry why I was late.
The railings were splendid in black and in gold
And I tied up the horses and walked in the cold
Across the wide courtyard; the steps were so broad,
And someone in frockcoat said, 'Ticket, my Lord?'
I felt in my pocket – I knew it was there –
Mixed up with dog biscuits, and apple and pear.
And I bowed to the queen, and would you believe,
I remembered to cover the hole in my sleeve.
The queen very graciously chose not to see
The string round my trousers, the tear at my knee.
Ferdinand, Ferdinand,
What did you there?
I knelt to the queen and she touched my grey hair.

Gregory Harrison

Lightships

All night long when the wind is high
Nnn nnn nnnn
The lightships moan and moan to the sky
Nnn nnn nnnn.

Their foghorns whine when the mist runs free
Nnn nnn nnnn
Warning the men on the ships at sea
Nnn nnn nnnn.

Clive Sansom

Swim, Swan!

Swan swam over the sea,
    Swim, swan, swim!
Swan swam back again,
Well swum, swan!

Anon.

Little Billy Tailor

Little Billy Tailor
Gone to be a sailor,
His ship's for China bound;
Won't the sea perplex him!
Won't its rolling vex him!
I hope he won't get drowned.

Anon.

Me – Pirate

If ever I go to sea,
I think I'll be a pirate:
I'll have a treasure-ship in tow
And a man-of-war to fire at.

With a cutlass at my belt,
And a pistol in my hand,
I'll nail my Crossbones to the mast
And sail for a foreign land.

And when we reach that shore,
We'll beat our battle-drum
And fire a salute of fifteen guns
To tell them we have come.

We'll fight them all day long;
We'll seize their chests of gold,
Their diamonds, coins and necklaces,
And stuff them in our hold.

A year and a day at home,
Then off on the waves again –
Lord of the Caribbean Seas
King of the Spanish Main!

Clive Sansom

A Long Blue Dragon

The Shark

The shark
Swims
In the dark
Of the deep
Its eye gleams
As it sees
Streams
Of gold fish –
Bold fish
Swimming too near
For the shark is well aware
That here
Is a tasty dish
Of fish
And the shark lies
In wait –
No fisherman,
No flies
No bait.
And the fish swim past
The shark follows –
Fast,
And swallows.

Lalla Ward

The Dark Wood

In the dark, dark wood, there was
  a dark, dark house,
And in that dark, dark house, there was
  a dark, dark room,
And in that dark, dark room, there was
  a dark, dark cupboard,
And in that dark, dark cupboard, there was
  a dark, dark shelf,
And on that dark, dark shelf, there was
  a dark, dark box,
And in that dark, dark box, there was a
  GHOST!

Anon.

The Donkey

My mother bought a donkey – she thought it was a cow.
She sent me out to milk it, but I didn't know how.
The night was dark and I couldn't see,
And that old donkey took a bite out of me.

Anon.

Little Dick

Little Dick he was so quick,
He rushed to the window from his bed.
He bent his bow to shoot a crow
And shot the pussy-cat's tail instead.

Anon.

A Ham-bone and some Jellied Eels

A ham-bone and some jellied eels went knocking on a door,
They had just crept out of the grocery store,
The lady went upstairs to get a gun,
And you should have seen them jump and run.

Anon.

Twenty-five Robbers

Friday night at half past eight,
Twenty-five robbers came knocking on my gate.
I went out and let them in
And I hit each one with my rolling-pin.

Anon.

The Dreaded Tootsie-Kana

When the Tootsie-Kana comes,
Hide yourself behind your thumbs;
Tie a dustbin on your head;
Stay indoors; go to bed.

When the Tootsie-Kana goes,
Peel an apple with your toes;
Buy a sausage; paint it red –
Tootsie-Kana falls down dead.

Spike Milligan

The Hare

Between the valley and the hill
There sat a little hare;
It nibbled at the grass until
The ground was nearly bare.

And when the ground was nearly bare
It rested in the sun;
A hunter came and saw it there
And shot it with his gun.

It thought it must be dead, be dead,
But, wonderful to say,
It found it was alive instead
And quickly ran away.

Rose Fyleman

Have you seen the Hidebehind?

Have you seen the Hidebehind?
I don't think you will, mind you,
because as you're running through the dark
the Hidebehind's behind you.

Michael Rosen

Hog-pig waits on a mountain

Hog-pig waits on a mountain
   above a valley in the spring.
Hog-pig waits on a mountain
   above the valley where he is king.

He could – if he would
   chew up churches and trees
   ram his tusks through castle walls
   and bite through men-in-armour
   like a dog cracking fleas.

Hog-pig could trumpet in the air
   and make the valleys roar
or wait up on the mountain
   as he's always done before.

Michael Rosen

Heltery-Skeltery

Run, rabbit, run!
Run to your warren!
The harvest is done,
The meadow is barren.
The corn was your shelter
From stone, stick and gun,
Heltery, Skeltery,
Run, rabbit, run!

Eleanor Farjeon

A Monstrous Mouse

Just as I'd sucked in wind to take
A giant puff at my birthday cake,

While all the children sang and cheered,
Up shot the window shade – in peered

A monstrous mouse with jagged jaws!
Into the kitchen poked two paws

With fingernails like reindeer antlers!
The way a team of house-dismantlers

Bash houses down with a swinging ball,
He kicked – boom! – no more kitchen wall –

And through a new door to our kitchen
That wicked mouse, his whiskers twitchin',

Grabbed hold of my cake plate by both handles
And shouted, 'Yum! what nice hot candles!'

Straight through my cake his head went – squish!
I didn't have time to make a wish.

But when he pulled himself back out,
All fresh fruit frosting, his whole snout

Was fire! Sparks sputtered from each whisker!
You never did see mouse-dancing brisker.

Thick clouds of smoke choked our apartment.
My father phoned the Fire Department.

Up screeched four fire trucks, sirens roaring –
Nobody found *my* party boring!

Our bowl of orangeade and ice
Proved just the thing for dunking mice.

Mouse ran outside and down his tunnel
Faster than water through a funnel.

I sort of forget what games we played.
Nobody drank much orangeade.

X. J. Kennedy

The Ugstabuggle

Over by my bedroom wall
The ugstabuggle stands,
A monster nearly nine feet tall
With hairy, grasping hands.
In afternoons and mornings
He's always out of sight,
But often I can see him
In the darkness late at night.
Yet when I do not think of him
He disappears again,
And when I sleep he goes, because
I cannot see him then!

Peter Wesley-Smith

Green Man, Blue Man

As I was walking through Guildhall Square
I smiled to see a green man there,
But when I saw him coming near
My heart was filled with nameless fear.

As I was walking through Madford Lane
A blue man stood there in the rain.
I asked him in by my front-door,
For I'd seen a blue man before.

As I was walking through Landlake Wood
A grey man in the forest stood,
But when he turned and said, 'Good day'
I shook my head and ran away.

As I was walking by Church Stile
A purple man spoke there a while.
I spoke to him because, you see,
A purple man once lived by me.

But when the night falls dark and fell
How, O how, am I to tell,
Grey man, green man, purple, blue,
Which is which is which of you?

Charles Causley

A Thousand Hairy Savages

A thousand hairy savages
Sitting down to lunch
Gobble gobble glup glup
Munch munch munch

Spike Milligan

Bump

Things that go 'bump!' in the night,
Should not really give one a fright.
It's the hole in each ear
That lets in the fear,
That and the absence of light!

Spike Milligan

Creeping

A long blue dragon
  Is creeping through the village.
He's lashing his tail,
  And he's tossing his head.
Run, little children,
  Run into your houses;
Run into your houses,
  And jump into bed! . . .

Hilda Adams

Upstairs, downstairs

Upstairs, downstairs,
Creeping like a mouse,
Creeping in the darkness
Round and round the house.
Creep, creep, creeping,
Round and round about –
I hope the wind won't come inside
And blow my candle out.

Evelyn Abraham

The Three Mice

Three mice went into a hole to spin,
Puss passed by and she peeped in:
'What are you doing, my little men?'
'Weaving coats for gentlemen.'
'Please let me come in to wind off your thread.'
'Oh no, Mistress Pussy, you'll bite off our heads.'

Says Puss: 'You look so wondrous wise,
I like your whiskers and bright black eyes,
Your house is the nicest house I see,
I think there is room for you and me.'
The mice were so pleased that they opened the door,
And pussy soon laid them all dead on the floor.

Anon.

Oh, Who will Wash the Tiger's Ears?

Two Cats

When we opened the door late
to see what had happened to the sky
there were two cats
crouching among the snowdunes
pretending they were fireside laps.
The beads in their eyes stole some of
our kitchen light
and spilt it on to the path.
So we put down the bones of a chop there too
saying: there's some marrow inside that you know –
but they didn't believe it was for them
and sat still thawing their patches
like two warm loaves
and groaning that we hadn't put it near enough
seeing that they had put their feet to bed by now.

Michael Rosen

The Young Puppy

There was a young puppy called Howard,
Who at fighting was rather a coward;
  He never quite ran
  When the battle began,
But he started at once to bow-wow hard.

A. A. Milne

Higglety, pigglety, pop!

Higglety, pigglety, pop!
The dog has eaten the mop;
The pig's in a hurry,
The cat's in a flurry,
Higglety, pigglety, pop!

Anon.

Three Little Chickens

Said the first little chicken,
With a queer little squirm,
'Oh, I wish I could find
A fat little worm!'

Said the second little chicken,
With a little sigh of grief,
'Oh, I wish I could find
A little green leaf!'

Said the third little chicken,
With a sharp little squeal,
'Oh, I wish I could find
Some nice yellow meal!'

'Now, see here,' said their mother
From the green garden patch,
'If you want any breakfast,
You must all come and scratch!'

Anon.

I had a little moppet

I had a little moppet
And put it in my pocket
   And fed it on corn and hay.
There came a proud beggar
And swore he would have her,
   And stole my poor moppet away.
And through the wild wood she ran, ran, ran,
And through the wild wood she ran;
And all the long winter
She followed the hunter
   And never was heard of again.

Anon.

The Cow

The friendly cow all red and white,
   I love with all my heart;
She gives me cream with all her might,
   To eat with apple-tart.

She wanders lowing here and there,
   And yet she cannot stray,
All in the pleasant open air,
   The pleasant light of day;

And blown by all the winds that pass
   And wet with all the showers,
She walks among the meadow grass
   And eats the meadow flowers.

Robert Louis Stevenson

A Whale of a Tea-Time

Algernon Snail
Caught a very fine whale,
    And took it indoors for his tea;
But the end of this tale
Is the whale ate the snail –
    So the whale took the snail in for tea.

Carey Blyton

I went up the high hill

I went up the high hill,
There I saw a climbing goat;
I went down by the running rill,
There I saw a ragged sheep;
I went out to the roaring sea,
There I saw a tossing boat;
I went under the green tree,
There I saw two doves asleep.

Anon.

The Manatee

The sea-cow or grey manatee
Spends most of its time in the sea;
   But in tropical rainstorms
   It suffers from brainstorms
And hangs upside down in a tree.

Carey Blyton

My Animals

My animals are made of wool and glass,
Also of wood. Table and mantelpiece
Are thickly covered with them. It's because
You cannot keep real cats or dogs in these

High-up new flats. I really want to have
A huge, soft marmalade or, if not that,
Some animal that *seems* at least to love.
Hamsters? A dog? No, what I need's a cat.

I hate a word like 'pets'; it sounds so much
Like something with no living of its own.
And yet each time that I caress and touch
My wool or glass ones, I feel quite alone.

No kittens in our flat, no dogs to bark
Each time the bell rings. Everything is still;
Often I want a zoo, a whole Noah's ark.
Nothing is born here, nothing tries to kill.

Elizabeth Jennings

At the Zoo

First I saw the white bear, then I saw the black;
Then I saw the camel with a hump upon his back;
Then I saw the grey wolf, with mutton in his maw;
Then I saw the wombat waddle in the straw;
Then I saw the elephant a-waving of his trunk;
Then I saw the monkeys – mercy, how unpleasantly they – smelt!

William Makepeace Thackeray

The Elephant

The elephant carries a great big trunk;
He never packs it with clothes;
It has no lock and it has no key,
But he takes it wherever he goes.

Anon.

A Tomcat

Oh, the funniest thing I've ever seen
Was a tomcat sewing on a sewing machine.
Oh, the sewing machine got running too slow,
And it took seven stitches in the tomcat's toe.

Anon.

Drumming

Tum-tumpty-tum,
The cat is playing the drum;
Four little mice are shaking the ground,
Dancing merrily round and round,
Tum-tumpty-tum.

Tum-tumpty-tum,
The cat is playing the drum;
Three little mice are shaking the ground,
Dancing merrily round and round,
Tum-tumpty-tum.

Tum-tumpty-tum,
The cat is playing the drum;
Two little mice are shaking the ground,
Dancing merrily round and round,
Tum-tumpty-tum.

Tum-tumpty-tum,
The cat is playing the drum;
One little mouse is shaking the ground,
Dancing merrily round and round,
Tum-tumpty-tum.

Tum-tumpty-tum,
The cat is playing the drum;
No little mice are shaking the ground,
Dancing, dancing round and round,
Tum-tumpty-tum.

Anon.

from The Hedgehog

There's a hedgehog in the garden – come and see.
When he's still, he's like a pincushion that breathes.
When he moves, he's like a fat freckled mouse, following me
All over the place with pitter-patter feet.
He snorts and snuffs and sniffs my shoe,
Then hauls himself over the rise.

We'll introduce him to the cat. But she runs away
Into the box-tree, all hidden save her eyes
And nose and twitching tail –
Then suddenly leaps out and pounces.
(Can you blame her? He's drunk all
Her saucerful of milk, three fluid ounces.)

Caught?
Not likely. She pulls up short
And dances and prances and saws
The air all round him, mighty dainty with her paws;
Then, defeated, slinks away
To sulk or chase less prickly prey.

It's chilly now and getting late.
We'll cover him with a pile of autumn leaves
And let him hide or even hibernate.
In the morning we'll creep
Over the lawn and part the leaves and peer
Inside, and see if he's lying there asleep.
I hope he is . . .

He wasn't. He was out of his heap,
Waiting for me – wide awake perhaps all night? –
And came running towards me and round me and after me
All over the place with pitter-patter feet. . . .

Ian Serraillier

If I had a Donkey

If I had a donkey
That wouldn't go
D'you think I'd wallop him?
No! No! No!
I'd put him in a stable
And keep him nice and warm,
The best little donkey
That ever was born.
Gee up, Neddy,
Gee up, Neddy,
The best little donkey
That ever was born.

Anon.

The Caterpillar

Little Arabella Miller
Found a furry caterpillar,
And let it crawl upon her mother,
Then upon her baby brother;
Both cried, 'Naughty Arabella,
Take away the caterpillar.'

Anon.

Five Little Monkeys

Five little monkeys walked along the shore;
One went a-sailing,
Then there were four.
Four little monkeys climbed up a tree;
One of them tumbled down,
Then there were three.
Three little monkeys found a pot of glue;
One got stuck in it,
Then there were two.
Two little monkeys found a currant bun;
One ran away with it,
Then there was one.
One little monkey cried all afternoon,
So they put him in an aeroplane
And sent him to the moon.

Anon.

My Garden

Rabbits and moles
Always make holes.

It's a rabbit habit.

But the moles should be told
That my lawn is all-holed.

Barbara Ireson

Squirrel

The squirrel in the hickory tree's a
nervous fellow,
all quiver and scurry.
See him

hurl himself upon
a limb
worry a nut
pack his cheeks
race
downtree
to a secret place and
hurry
back
in furry frenzy.

There's something he knows
that makes him
go,
this soft slow
mellow
autumn day.

It has to do with
hunger
in the snow.

Lilian Moore

Dogs

The dogs I know
Have many shapes
For some are big and tall,
　And some are long,
　　And
　　some
　　are thin,
And some are fat and small.
And some are little bits of fluff
And have no shape at all.

Marchette Chute

Cat

The black cat yawns,
Opens her jaws,
Stretches her legs,
And shows her claws.

Then she gets up
And stands on four
Long stiff legs
And yawns some more.

She shows her sharp teeth,
She stretches her lip,
Her slice of a tongue
Turns up at the tip.

Lifting herself
On her delicate toes,
She arches her back
As high as it goes.

She lets herself down
With particular care,
And pads away
With her tail in the air.

Mary B. Miller

Furry Bear

If I were a bear
   And a big bear too,
I shouldn't much care
   If it froze or snew;
I shouldn't much mind
   If it snowed or friz –
I'd be all fur-lined
   With a coat like his!

For I'd have fur boots and a brown fur wrap,
And brown fur knickers and a big fur cap.
I'd have a fur muffle-ruff to cover my jaws,
And brown fur mittens on my big brown paws.
With a big brown furry-down up to my head,
I'd sleep all winter in a big fur bed.

A. A. Milne

Oliphaunt

Grey as a mouse,
Big as a house,
Nose like a snake,
I make the earth shake,
As I tramp through the grass;
Trees crack as I pass.
With horns in my mouth
I walk in the South,
Flapping big ears.
Beyond count of years
I stump round and round,
Never lie on the ground,
Not even to die.
Oliphaunt am I,
Biggest of all,
Huge, old, and tall.
If ever you'd met me,
You wouldn't forget me.
If you never do,
You won't think I'm true;
But old Oliphaunt am I,
And I never lie.

J. R. R. Tolkien

Oh, Who will wash the Tiger's Ears?

Oh, who will wash the tiger's ears?
And who will comb his tail?
And who will brush his sharp white teeth?
And who will file his nails?

Oh, Bobby may wash the tiger's ears
And Susy may file his nails
And Lucy may brush his long white teeth
And I'll go down for the mail.

Shel Silverstein

I had a cow that gave rich milk

I had a cow that gave rich milk.
I made her a bonnet of dainty silk,
I fed her on the finest hay
And milked her twenty times a day.

Anon.

My Little Hen

I once had a little hen that never gave me eggs,
So I made her a coat and put stockings on her legs
And I gave her corn that I fetched from the store,
Then she laid ten big brown eggs just at my kitchen door.

Anon.

The Frog's Lament

'I can't bite
like a dog,'
said the bright
green frog.

'I can't dig,
I can't squirt,
I can't grip,
I can't hurt.

'All I can do
is hop and hide
when enemies come
from far and wide.

'I can't scratch
like a cat.
I'm no match
for a rat.

'I can't stab,
I can't snare,
I can't grab,
I can't scare.

'All I can do
my whole life through
is hop,' said the frog,
'and hide from view.'

And that's
what I saw him
up and do.

Aileen Fisher

The Mouse in the Wainscot

Hush, Suzanne!
Don't lift your cup.
That breath you heard
Is a mouse getting up.

As the mist that steams
From your milk as you sup,
So soft is the sound
Of a mouse getting up.

There! did you hear
His feet pitter-patter,
Lighter than tipping
Of beads in a platter,

And then like a shower
On the window pane
The little feet scampering
Back again?

O falling of feather!
O drift of a leaf!
The mouse in the wainscot
Is dropping asleep.

Ian Serraillier

Bird Talk

Five little owls

Five little owls in an old elm-tree,
Fluffy and puffy as owls could be,
Blinking and winking with big round eyes
At the big round moon that hung in the skies:
As I passed beneath, I could hear one say,
'There'll be mouse for supper, there will, to-day!'
Then all of them hooted 'Tu-whit, Tu-whoo!
Yes, mouse for supper, Hoo hoo, Hoo hoo!'

Anon.

Pigeon and Wren

Coo, coo, coo!
It's as much as a pigeon
  Can do
To bring up two!
But the little wren
  Can manage ten,
And bring them up
  Like gentlemen!

Anon.

Green

Ducklings,
Look around.

That's treegreen
filling the sky

and there's grassgreen
running
up the hill
steeply.

The shadowgreen is
pine woods,
dark
old.

The yellowgreen is
young leaf
unfolding,
new
as you.

Breathe green
deeply.

Lilian Moore

Old Mother Minchin

Old Mother Minchin
When she was wed
Wanted to live
In a watercress bed.

Straw to sit on,
And reeds to press,
There she sat
In her Sunday dress!

What a peculiar
Thing to do!
But old Mother Minchin
Wasn't like you:

With a feather as strong
As a fine quill pen –
Old Mother Minchin,
My little moorhen!

Jean Kenward

Birds on a Stone

There were two birds
  Sat on a stone.
One flew away,
  Then there was one.
The other flew after,
  Then there was none,
And so the poor stone
Was left all alone.

Anon.

Hen's Song

Chick, chick, come out of your shell,
I've warmed you long and I've warmed you well;
The sun is hot and the sky is blue
Quick, chick, it's time you came through.

Rose Fyleman

Three Grey Geese

Three grey geese in a green field grazing:
In a green field grazing are three grey geese.
The grey geese graze while I am gazing:
I gaze and gaze till the grey geese cease.

Anon.

Ducky-Daddles

Ducky-Daddles
Loves the puddles.
How he waddles
As he paddles
In the puddles –
Ducky Daddles!

W. Kingdon-Ward

The Merle and the Blackbird

The merle and the blackbird,
The laverock and the lark,
The plover and the lapwing –
How many birds is that?

Anon.

(Answer: three, because
merle and blackbird are the same
laverock and lark are the same
plover and lapwing are the same.)

The Last Word of a Bluebird
as Told to a Child

As I went out a Crow
In a low voice said, 'Oh,
I was looking for you.
How do you do?
I just came to tell you
To tell Lesley (will you?)
That her little Bluebird
Wanted me to bring word
That the north wind last night
That made the stars bright
And made ice on the trough
Almost made him cough
His tail feathers off.
He just had to fly!
But he sent her Good-bye,
And said to be good,
And wear her red hood,
And look for skunk tracks
In the snow with an axe –
And do everything!
And perhaps in the spring
He would come back and sing.'

Robert Frost

There was an old lady of France

There was an old lady of France
Who taught little ducklings to dance;
When she said, 'Tick-a-tack!' they only said 'Quack!'
Which grieved that old lady of France.

Edward Lear

I saw eight magpies in a tree

I saw eight magpies in a tree,
Two for you and six for me:

One for sorrow, two for mirth,
Three for a wedding, four for a birth,

Five for England, six for France,
Seven for a fiddler, eight for a dance.

Anon.

Quack

The duck is whiter than whey is,
His tail tips up over his back,
The eye in his head is as round as a button,
And he says, *Quack! Quack!*

He swims on his bright blue mill-pond,
By the willow-tree under the shack,
Then stands on his head to see down to the bottom,
And says, *Quack! Quack!*

When Molly steps out of the kitchen,
For apron – pinned round with a sack –
He squints at her round face, her dish, and what's in it,
And says, *Quack! Quack!*

He preens the pure snow of his feathers
In the sun by the wheat-straw stack;
At dusk waddles home with his brothers and sisters,
And says, *Quack! Quack!*

Walter de la Mare

Time to Rise

A birdie with a yellow bill
Hopped upon the window sill,
Cocked his shining eye and said:
'Ain't you 'shamed, you sleepy-head!'

Robert Louis Stevenson

Near and Far

What do hens say
With all their talking?
What luck! What luck! they cluck,
Look, look! they say
As they settle
In a sunny nook
And scoop
Dust under their feathers.

What does the ditch digging machine
Chatter about
Scratching
Into the dirt?
Who do I thank
For these scrumptious
Scrunchy
Chunks of rock? it asks
With a clatter and clank
As it stacks the cool earth up
In a neat brown bank.

Only in summer
The big machine
And loose old hens
Play the same scooping
Sunny game,
Saying the same things over and over
At about the same loudness
Because the machine is farther away.

Harry Behn

These Storks are Here to be Seen

There are storks
here you certainly
know it you hear them chatter
          and bicker
          and flutter
          and jabber
          and jostle
          and babble
          and cackle
          and cuddle
          and chortle
You build a sanctuary
and ask them to move, please.
Ask them to be a little quieter

if they will.

Carl Bagge

Eggs are laid by turkeys

Eggs are laid by turkeys
Eggs are laid by hens
Eggs are laid by robins
Eggs are laid by wrens
Eggs are laid by eagles
Eggs are laid by quail,
Pigeons, parrots, peregrines:
And that's how every bird begins.

Mary Ann Hoberman

Dead Blackbird

The blackbird used to come each day
listening, head-sideways, for movement under the lawn,
stabbing his yellow-as-crocus bill
precisely in,
pulling out a pink elastic worm.

In winter with flirted tail
he landed on the sill for crumbs
ousting sparrows, blue-tits – even robins.
Soot-black, sleek,
his plumage shone like a dark man's head.

Phoebe Hesketh

Bird Talk

'Think . . .' said the robin,
'Think . . .' said the jay,
sitting in the garden,
talking one day.

'Think about people –
the way they grow:
they don't have feathers
at all, you know.

They don't eat beetles,
they don't grow wings,
they don't like sitting
on wires and things.'
'Think !' said the robin.
'Think !' said the jay.
'Aren't people funny
to be that way?'

Aileen Fisher

The Swallows

Nine swallows sat on a telephone wire:
'Teeter, teeter,' and then they were still,
all facing one way, with the sun like a fire
along their blue shoulders, and hot on each bill.
But they sat there so quietly, all of the nine,
that I almost forgot they were swallows at all.
They seemed more like clothespins left out on the line
when the wash is just dried, and the first raindrops fall.

Elizabeth Coatsworth

In the Garden

Greedy little sparrow,
  Great big crow,
Saucy little tom-tits
  All in a row.

Are you very hungry,
  No place to go?
Come and eat my breadcrumbs,
  In the snow.

Anon.

That's the Way the Money Goes

Choosing Shoes

New shoes, new shoes,
Red and pink and blue shoes,
Tell me what would *you* choose
If they'd let us buy?

Buckle shoes, bow shoes,
Pretty pointy-toe shoes,
Strappy, cappy low shoes;
Let's have some to try.

Bright shoes, white shoes,
Dandy dance-by-night shoes,
Perhaps-a-little-tight shoes;
Like some? So would I.
BUT
Flat shoes, fat shoes,
Stump-along-like-that shoes,
Wipe-them-on-the-mat shoes
O that's the sort they'll buy.

Ffrida Wolfe

At the Super-market

Take a trolley,
  Push it round,
Castor sugar?
  Get a pound.
There's the cocoa,
  Take a tin.
Here's a loaf,
  But it's cut thin.
There's another.
  That will do.
Now we'll find
  Some jam for you.
Choose a jar.
  Yes, strawberry
Will suit your Dad
  And also me.
A tin of fish,
  A bag of rice,
That cream-filled cake
  Looks very nice.

We must have soap
  And toothpaste too,
This green shampoo
  Will do for you.
Apples and pears and
  Two pounds of peas,
A cabbage, a swede
  And a turnip, please.
I nearly forgot
  My jar of honey.
I wonder if we
  Have got enough money?
Push the trolley
  To the till.
I'll fetch a box
  For you to fill.
Leave the empty
  Trolley here.
My purse is empty
  Too, I fear.

Barbara Ireson

Coming from the Fair

Coming from the fair!
  Coming from the fair!
    We bought a little bottle
      For our baby over there;
        Alas, for we broke it,
          And we tried to buy another,
            But all the shops were closed,
              So we hurried home to mother.

Translated from a Chinese nursery rhyme *by I. T. Headland*

Gee up, Neddy

Gee up, Neddy, to the fair;
What shall we buy when we get there?
A penny apple and a penny pear;
Gee up, Neddy, to the fair.

Anon.

Banbury Fair

As I was going to Banbury,
  Upon a summer's day,
My dame had butter, eggs and fruit,
  And I had corn and hay.
Joe drove the ox, and Tom the swine,
  Dick took the foal and mare;
I sold them all – then home to dine,
  From famous Banbury Fair.

Anon.

Giddy Girls, Noisy Boys

Giddy girls, noisy boys,
   Come and buy my painted toys;
    Medals made of gingerbread,
      And penny horses white and red.

Anon.

Home From the Carnival

Gone all the lights and all the noise,
Gone all the cotton candy's joys,
And all my money spent and gone
With all the rides I rode upon
And all my money gone and spent
Upon the tables in the tent:
The Wheel of Fortune clicked and spun –
I lost my dimes and nothing won,
Not even from the bottom shelf.
I bring home nothing but myself,
And take to bed with meagre cheer
The teddy bear I won last year.

Russell Hoban

All for a Farthing

I went into my grandmother's garden,
And there I found a farthing.
I went into my next door neighbour's;
There I bought
A pipkin and a popkin,
A slipkin and a slopkin,
A nailboard, a sailboard,
And all for a farthing.

Anon.

Pop Goes the Weasel

Up and down the City Road,
    In and out the Eagle;
That's the way the money goes –
    Pop goes the weasel!

Half a pound of tuppenny rice,
    Half a pound of treacle;
Mix it up and make it nice –
    Pop goes the weasel!

Every night when I go out
    The monkey's on the table;
Take a stick and knock it off –
    Pop goes the weasel!

Anon.

If only I had plenty of money

If only I had plenty of money,
I'd buy you some flowers, and I'd buy you some honey,
I'd buy you a boat, and I'd buy you a sail,
I'd buy you a cat with a long bushy tail,
I'd buy you a brooch and a bangle as well,
I'd buy you a church, and I'd buy you the bell,
I'd buy you the earth, I'd buy you the moon –
Oh money, dear money, please come very soon.

Paul Edmonds

The Grocers

One grocer worked hard weighing rice,
Two grocers worked hard packing spice,
Three grocers worked hard sorting teas,
Four grocers worked hard wrapping cheese.
Five grocers worked hard stacking jam,
Six grocers worked hard slicing ham,
Seven grocers worked hard cutting meats,
Eight grocers worked hard opening sweets,
Nine grocers worked hard selling bread,
Ten grocers, tired out, went home to bed.

Barbara Ireson

The Friendly Cinnamon Bun

Shining in his stickiness and glistening with honey,
Safe among his sisters and his brothers on a tray,
With raisin eyes that looked at me as I put down my money,
There smiled a friendly cinnamon bun, and this I heard him say:

'It's a lovely, lovely morning, and the world's a lovely place;
I know it's going to be a lovely day.
I know we're going to be good friends; I like your honest face;
Together we might go a long, long way.'

The baker's girl rang up the sale, 'I'll wrap your bun,' said she.
'Oh no, you needn't bother,' I replied.
I smiled back at that cinnamon bun and ate him, one two three,
And walked out with his friendliness inside.

Russell Hoban

Come Christmas

Christmas Stocking

What will go into the Christmas Stocking
While the clock on the mantlepiece goes tick-tocking?
    An orange, a penny,
    Some sweets, not too many,
    A trumpet, a dolly,
    A sprig of red holly,
    A book and a top
    And a grocery shop,
    Some beads in a box,
    An ass and an ox
    And a lamb, plain and good,
    All whittled in wood,
    A white sugar dove,
    A handful of love,
    Another of fun,
    And it's very near done –
    A big silver star
    On top – there you are!
Come morning you'll wake to the clock's tick-tocking,
And that's what you'll find in the Christmas Stocking.

Eleanor Farjeon

The Pieman

As I was going down Mincing Lane,
Mincing Lane on a Christmas Day,
'Hot mince pies!' a pieman cries,
'Two for a penny, and look at the size!'

Anon.

On Christmas Day

There was a pig
Went out to dig,
Christmas Day, Christmas Day,
There was a pig
Went out to dig
On Christmas Day in the morning.

There was a sow
Went out to plough,
Christmas Day, Christmas Day,
There was a sow
Went out to plough
On Christmas Day in the morning.

There was a sparrow
Went out to harrow,
Christmas Day, Christmas Day,
There was a sparrow
Went out to harrow
On Christmas Day in the morning.

There was a crow
Went out to sow,
Christmas Day, Christmas Day,
There was a crow
Went out to sow
On Christmas Day in the morning.

There was a sheep
Went out to reap,
Christmas day, Christmas Day,
There was a sheep
Went out to reap
On Christmas Day in the morning.

Anon.

Christmas Pudding

Take milk, eggs, and raisins.
Take milk, eggs, and raisins; suet and
    sugar and flour.
Take milk, eggs, and raisins; suet and
    sugar and flour; candied-peel and breadcrumbs.
Take milk, eggs, and raisins; suet and
    sugar and flour; candied-peel and breadcrumbs -
    and boil for eight hours.

Anon.

It was a stormy night

It was a stormy night
One Christmas day
as they fell awake
on the Sante Fe

Turkey, jelly
and the ship's old cook
all jumped out
of a recipe book

The jelly wobbled
the turkey gobbled
and after them both
the old cook hobbled

Gobbler gobbled
Hobbler's Wobbler.
Hobbler gobbled
Wobbler's Gobbler.

Gobbly-gobbler
gobbled Wobbly
Hobbly-hobbler
Gobbled Gobbly.

Gobble gobbled
Hobble's Wobble
Hobble gobbled
gobbled Wobble.

gobble gobble
wobble wobble
hobble gobble
wobble gobble

Michael Rosen

Carol of the Brown King

Of the three Wise Men
Who came to the King,
One was a brown man,
So they sing.

Of the three Wise Men
Who followed the Star,
One was a brown king
From afar.

They brought fine gifts
Of spices and gold
In jewelled boxes
Of beauty untold.

Unto His humble
Manger they came
And bowed their heads
In Jesus' name.

Three Wise Men,
One dark like me –
Part of His
Nativity.

Langston Hughes

Uncle John's Pig

When Uncle John brought home the pig on Christmas
    afternoon,
It didn't look like anything except a burst balloon,
A wiggly waggly pinky rag, as limp as limp could be;
'Call that a pig?' said little Jane: said Uncle, 'Wait and see.'

He blew into the pig and soon we saw it filling out;
He blew again and then we saw four legs, a little snout;
He blew once more, and then we saw the curly tail so neat,
He screwed it up and there it stood, the Perfect Pig complete.

A pig to join in any game so steady and so stout;
Then sometimes Uncle John, for fun would let the air run out,
And then we'd see it shrivel up and sink down dead – and then
Kind Uncle John would laugh and blow it back to life again.

But after Uncle John had gone (he went on Boxing Night),
Said Jane, 'Let's make it bigger now,' and soon she'd blown it
    tight;
She puffed and blew, and still it grew so big, so big, so BIG,
That with a mighty BANG . . . it burst . . . Oh, how I missed
    that pig!

Ffrida Wolfe

Advice to a child

Set your fir-tree
In a pot;
Needles green
Is all it's got.
Shut the door
And go away,
And so to sleep
Till Christmas Day.
In the morning
Seek your tree,
And you shall see
What you shall see.

Hang your stocking
By the fire,
Empty of
Your heart's desire;
Up the chimney
Say your say,
And so to sleep
Till Christmas Day.
In the morning
Draw the blind,
And you shall find
What you shall find.

Eleanor Farjeon

Little Tree

little tree
little silent Christmas tree
you are so little
you are more like a flower

who found you in the green forest
and were you very sorry to come away?
see i will comfort you
because you smell so sweetly

i will kiss your cool bark
and hug you safe and tight
just as your mother would,
only don't be afraid

look at the spangles
that sleep all the year in a dark box
dreaming of being taken out
              and allowed to shine,
the balls the chains red
          and gold the fluffy threads,

put up your little arms
and i'll give them all to you to hold
every finger shall have its ring
and there won't be a single place
                    dark or   happy

then when you're quite dressed
you'll stand in the window
              for everyone to see
and how they'll stare!
oh but you'll be very proud

and my little sister and i will take hands
and looking up at our beautiful tree
we'll dance and sing
'Noel Noel'

                        e. e. cummings

In the Week When Christmas Comes

This is the week when Christmas comes.

Let every pudding burst with plums,
And every tree bear dolls and drums,
   In the week when Christmas comes.

Let every hall have boughs of green,
With berries glowing in between,
   In the week when Christmas comes.

Let every doorstep have a song
Sounding the dark street along,
   In the week when Christmas comes.

Let every steeple ring a bell
With a joyful tale to tell,
   In the week when Christmas comes.

Let every night put forth a star
To show us where the heavens are,
   In the week when Christmas comes.

Let every stable have a lamb
Sleeping warm beside its dam
   In the week when Christmas comes.

This is the week when Christmas comes.

Eleanor Farjeon

Index of first lines

Rhyme Time 2

Chosen by Barbara Ireson

Illustrated by Lesley Smith

Contents

Okay Everybody,
Listen to This

Okay everybody, listen to this

Okay everybody, listen to this:
I am tired of being smaller
Than you
And them
And him
And trees and buildings.
So watch out
All you gorillas and adults
Beginning tomorrow morning
Boy
Am I going to be taller.

Karla Kuskin

Every few weeks someone looks at me

Every few weeks someone looks at me and says:
my you've grown
and then every few weeks someone says:
they've grown too long

and silver scissors come out of the drawer
and chip at my toes and run through my hair.

Now I don't like this one little bit.
I won't grow if I'm going to be chopped.
What's me is mine and I want to keep it
so either the scissors or my nails had better stop.

Michael Rosen

Hair

I despair
About hair
    With all the fuss
    For us
Of snipping
And clipping
    Of curling
    And twirling,
Of tying
And drying,
    And lopping
    And flopping,
And flurries
And worries,
    About strength,
    The length,
As it nears
The ears
    Or shoulder.
    When you're older
It turns grey
Or goes away
    Or leaves a fuzz
    Hair does!

Max Fatchen

I've had this shirt

I've had this shirt
that's covered in dirt
for years and years and years.

It used to be red
but I wore it in bed
and it went grey
'cos I wore it all day
for years and years and years.

The arms fell off
in the Monday wash
and you can see my vest
through the holes in the chest
for years and years and years.

As my shirt falls apart
I'll keep the bits
in a biscuit tin
on the mantelpiece
for years and years and years.

Michael Rosen

Hullabaloo!

Hullabaloo!
We'll race downstairs,
Splatter our porridge and bump the chairs,
And teach the budgie a thing or two!
Hullabalay baloo!

Hullabaloo!
We'll spend the day
In the most magnificent kind of way!
We'll shout whenever we want to shout,
And throw whatever we like about,
And turn the neighbourhood inside out!
Hullabaloo balay!

Hullabaloo!
The sun is high,
The clouds are shooshing across the sky,
Birds are soaring and winds are free,
Trees are tossing and we are WE!
(Nobody else we would rather be!)
Hullabalay baloo!

Hullabaloo!
The day is done.
We've had the funniest kind of fun,
And once for ever belied the fears
That morning laughter must end in tears,
. . . *We're* not crying! so sucks to you!
Hullabaloo . . . boohoo . . . boohoo!
Hullabaloo . . . boohoo!

Ursula Moray Williams

11

Tiptoe

Yesterday I skipped all day,
The day before I ran,
Today I'm going to tiptoe
Everywhere I can.
I'll tiptoe down the stairway.
I'll tiptoe through the door.
I'll tiptoe to the living room
And give an awful roar
And my father, who is reading,
Will jump up from his chair
And mumble something silly like
'I didn't see you there.'
I'll tiptoe to my mother
And give a little cough
And when she spins to see me
Why, I'll softly tiptoe off.
I'll tiptoe through the meadows,
Over hills and yellow sands
And when my toes get tired
Then I'll tiptoe on my hands.

Karla Kuskin

Every time I climb a tree

Every time I climb a tree
Every time I climb a tree
Every time I climb a tree
I scrape a leg
Or skin a knee
And every time I climb a tree
I find some ants
Or dodge a bee
And get the ants
All over me

And every time I climb a tree
Where have you been?
They say to me
But don't they know that I am free
Every time I climb a tree?
I like it best
To spot a nest
That has an egg
Or maybe three

And then I skin
The other leg
But every time I climb a tree
I see a lot of things to see
Swallows, rooftops and TV
And all the fields and farms there be
Every time I climb a tree
Though climbing may be good for ants
It isn't awfully good for pants
But still it's pretty good for me
Every time I climb a tree

David McCord

Eating an icicle, riding my bicycle

Eating an icicle, riding my bicycle,
Rolling along in the wind, rain and snow;
Chewing so happily, pedalling snappily
Backward and forward through gears high and low.
Icicle, bicycle, sometimes a tricycle,
Snappily, happily onward I go.

Anon

I found a silver dollar

I found a silver dollar,
But I had to pay the rent.
I found an alligator
But his steering-wheel was bent.
I found a little monkey,
So I took him to the zoo.
Then I found a sticky kiss and so
I brought it home to you.

Dennis Lee

Noise

I like noise.
The whoop of a boy, the thud of a hoof,
The rattle of rain on a galvanised roof,
The hub–bub of traffic, the roar of a train,
The throb of machinery numbing the brain,
The switching of wires in an overhead tram,
The rush of the wind, a door on the slam,
The boom of the thunder, the crash of the waves,
The din of a river that races and raves,
The crack of a rifle, the clank of a pail,
The strident tattoo of a swift slapping sail –
From any old sound that the silence destroys
Arises a gamut of soul–stirring joys.
I like noise.

J. Pope

Engineers

Pistons, valves and wheels and gears
That's the life of engineers
Thumping, chunking engines going
Hissing steam and whistles blowing.

There's not a place I'd rather be
Than working round machinery
Listening to that clanking sound
Watching all the wheels go round.

Jimmy Garthwaite

Do you or don't you

I like the tingling smell of tar,
And sticky ginger in a jar,
And drifting smoke from a cigar.
Do you?

I hate the stale damp smell of fogs
And matted hair of muddy dogs,
And slugs that lurk in stacked-up logs
Don't you?

I like the summer smell of sea,
And fishy smells about the quay
And strawberries and cream for tea.
Do you?

I hate the musty smell of mice,
And caged up birds, and uncooked rice,
And soft boiled eggs that aren't quite nice,
Don't you?

Anon

Mud

Mud is very nice to feel
All squishy-squash between the toes!
I'd rather wade in wiggly mud
Than smell a yellow rose.

Nobody else but the rosebush knows
How nice mud feels
Between the toes . . .

Polly Chase Boyden

My Dragon's Name is Jocelyn

Jocelyn, my dragon

My dragon's name is Jocelyn,
He's something of a joke.
For Jocelyn is very tame,
He doesn't like to maul or maim,
Or breathe a fearsome fiery flame;
He's much too smart to smoke.

And when I take him to the park
The children form a queue,
And say, 'What lovely eyes of red!'
As one by one they pat his head.
And Jocelyn is so well–bred,
He only eats a few!

Colin West

Under my bed

I've two large creatures under my bed
And no–one knows they're there.
I've fed them milk and fruit and bread
But did not stay to stare.

They've tails that lash
And teeth that gnash
And paws that thump
And heads that bump –

And I think I'll sleep in the shed.

Barbara Ireson

Advice to children

For a domestic, gentle pet,
A hippopotamus I'd get –
      They're very kind and mild.
I'm sure if you but purchase one
You'll find 'twill make a lot of fun
      For any little child.

Select one of a medium size,
With glossy fur and soft blue eyes,
      Then brush and comb him well.
With wreaths of flowers his forehead deck,
And from a ribbon round his neck
      Suspend a silver bell.

If it should be a rainy day,
Up in the nursery he will play
      With Baby, Tot and Ted;
Upon the rocking-horse he'll ride,
Or merrily he'll run and hide
      Beneath a chair or bed.

And when he wants to take a nap,
He'll cuddle up in Totty's lap,
      As quiet as a mouse.
Just try it, and you'll soon agree
A hippopotamus should be
      A pet in every house.

Carolyn Wells

Cottage

When I live in a Cottage
I shall keep in my Cottage

Two different Dogs,
Three creamy Cows,
Four giddy Goats,
Five pewter Pots,
Six silver Spoons,
Seven busy Beehives,
Eight ancient Appletrees,
Nine red Rosebushes,
Ten teeming Teapots,
Eleven chirping Chickens,
Twelve cosy Cats with their kittenish
  Kittens and
One Blessed Baby in a Basket.

That's what I'll have when I live in my Cottage . . .

Eleanor Farjeon

Thin dog

I've got a dog as thin as a rail,
He's got fleas all over his tail;
Every time his tail goes flop,
The fleas on the bottom all hop to the top.

Anon

My dog

My dog is such a gentle soul,
   Although he's big it's true.
He brings the paper in his mouth.
   He brings the postman too.

Max Fatchen

Suzie's new dog

Your dog? What dog? You mean it? – that!
   I was about to leave a note
Pinned to a fish to warn my cat
   To watch for a mouse in an overcoat!

So that's a dog! Is it any breed
   That anyone ever knew – or guessed?
Oh, a Flea Terrier! Yes indeed.
   Well now, I *am* impressed!

I guess no robber will try your house
   Or even cut through your yard.
Not when he knows you have a mouse
   – I mean a dog – like that on guard!

You have to go? I'm glad you came!
   I don't see a thing like that
Just every day. Does it have a name?
   Fang, eh? Well, I must warn my cat.

John Ciardi

Poor John

I really think it would be better
If John the postman with his letter
Did not come to number four
And try to put it through the door.
A dog with teeth as big as knives
Waits there for him and then it dives
And sinks those teeth into his sack
And snarls and barks till John runs back.
The only thing that John can do
Is leave the post at number two.

Barbara Ireson

I'll buy a peacock bird

When I have a beard that's curly and weird,
I'll buy myself a peacock bird.
He'll shout, 'Hello, hello, hello,'
As on my lawns he'll to and fro.
Other birds will hop and glare
As he sheds feathers here and there.

I'll ask my Aunty Maud to tea
(For she has swans and a maple tree)
To view my peacock on my lawn
Who shouts 'Hello' from break of dawn,
And spy his mantle spreading wide
All shimmering blue and golden-eyed.

Modwena Sedgwick

I wish

'I wish,'
Said Baby Bat,
'That I could
Get A Boy or Girl
To have me
For a pet.

We'd live
Inside this cold
Old cave
Safe from sunny weather,
Swooping out in
Darkest night
To feed on bugs
Together.

Then
Hanging in our
Cave we'd stay
Playing, upside down
All day!'

Lilian Moore

Cosy catnap

Pussy-kitten, pussy-cat,
purring on the kitchen mat,
How I like your furry tail
curl'd around you like a snail.

Pussy-kitten, pussy-cat,
purring on the kitchen mat;
fire tinkles in the grate,
clocks tick tip-toe, very late.

Pussy-kitten, pussy-cat,
purring on the kitchen mat;
hear the iron softly stamp
on steaming washing, warm and damp.

Pussy-kitten, pussy-cat,
purring on the kitchen mat,
squeeze your eyes right out of sight
and doze and blink and doze all night!

Pussy-kitten, pussy-cat,
purring on the kitchen mat;
purroo, purroo,
purroo, purroo,

Pussy-kitten, pussy-cat,
purrooing on the kitchen mat.

James Kirkup

Cat

The black cat yawns,
Opens her jaws,
Stretches her legs,
And shows her claws.

Then she gets up
And stands on four
Long stiff legs
And yawns some more.

She shows her sharp teeth,
She stretches her lip,
Her slice of tongue
Turns up at the tip.

Lifting herself
On her delicate toes,
She arches her back
As high as it goes.

She lets herself down
With particular care
And pads away
With her tail in the air.

Mary Britton Miller

Catnap

My cat sleeps
with her claws
clasped
and her long tail
curled.
My cat twitches
her tabby cheek
for the mice that
squeak
and the milk that
flows
by her pink, pink nose
in the purring warmth
of my cat's world.

Max Fatchen

Choosing their names

Our old cat has kittens three —
What do you think their names should be?

One is a tabby with emerald eyes,
    And a tail that's long and slender,
And into a temper she quickly flies
    If you ever by chance offend her,
        I think we shall call her this —
        I think we shall call her that —
Now, don't you think that Pepperpot
        Is a nice name for a cat?

One is black with a frill of white,
    And her feet are all white fur, too;
If you stroke her she carries her tail upright
    And quickly begins to purr, too!
        I think we shall call her this –
        I think we shall call her that –
Now, don't you think that Sootikin
        Is a nice name for a cat?

One is a tortoiseshell yellow and black,
    With plenty of white about him;
If you tease him, at once he sets up his back
    He's a quarrelsome one, ne'er doubt him.
        I think we shall call him this –
        I think we shall call him that –
Now, don't you think that Scratchaway
        Is a nice name for a cat?

Our old cat has kittens three
And I fancy these their names will be;
Pepperpot, Sootikin, Scratchaway – there!
Were ever kittens with these to compare?
And we call the old mother –
        Now, what do you think? –
    Tabitha Longclaws Tiddley Wink.

Thomas Hood

A kitten

He's nothing much but fur
And two round eyes of blue,
He has a giant purr
And a midget mew.

He darts and pats the air,
He starts and pricks his ear,
When there is nothing there
For him to see and hear.

He runs around in rings,
But why we cannot tell;
With sideways leaps he springs
At things invisible –

Then half-way through a leap
His started eyeballs close,
And he drops off to sleep
With one paw on his nose.

Eleanor Farjeon

Billy Booster

Billy Billy Booster
Had a little rooster,
The rooster died
And Billy cried.
Poor Billy Booster.

Anon

Missing

Has anybody seen my mouse?

I opened his box for half a minute,
Just to make sure he was really in it,
And while I was looking, he jumped outside!
I tried to catch him, I tried, I tried . . .
I think he's somewhere about the house.
Has *anyone* seen my mouse?

Uncle John, have you seen my mouse?

Just a small sort of mouse, a dear little brown one,
He came from the country, he wasn't a town one,
So he'll feel all lonely in a London Street;
Why, what could he possibly find to eat?

He must be somewhere, I'll ask Aunt Rose:
Have you seen a mouse with a woffelly nose?
Oh, somewhere about –
He's just got out . . .

Hasn't *anybody* seen my mouse?

A. A. Milne

Lost and found

LOST:
A Wizard's loving pet
Rather longish.
Somewhat scaly.
May be hungry or
upset.
Please feed daily.

P.S. Reward

FOUND:
A dragon
breathing fire.
Flails his scaly
tail
in ire.
Would eat twenty LARGE meals
daily
if we let him
Please
Come and get him.

P.S. No reward necessary.

Lilian Moore

puchction

to con
not hot
nut pot
in cat
put tin
no
on
inn
ton
cup

Goldfish

One small Fish in a
Polythene bag;
Can't swim round, can
Only look sad.
Take a pair of scissors,
Snip a quick hole:
Down flops water
And Fish into a bowl!

She waits a little moment,
Flips her tail free,
Then off into circles
As frisk as can be.
Dash–about – splash–about –
Do what you wish:
You're mine, you black-spotted
Cheeky–eyed
Fish!

John Walsh

Wanted

Has anyone got
A puppy to spare,
A cat or a rabbit
Or even a hare?

I'd cherish a pony,
I'd care for a horse,
If I'm offered a camel,
I'd love it, of course.

I'd take in a hamster,
I'd quite like a rat,
A toad would be welcome,
Or even a bat.

A beetle that's friendly
Would find that I'm kind,
Snake, lizard or earthworm,
I'm sure I don't mind.

I don't mind how big,
I don't mind how small,
I just want a pet
That can walk, fly or crawl.

Barbara Ireson

The Wiggley-Woggley Men

The Wiggley-Woggley men

Oh the Wiggley-Woggley men
They don't get up till ten
They run about
Then give a shout
And back to bed again!

Spike Milligan

Names

Murgatroyd Stephen Montgomery James.
Did you ever hear such a collection of names?
Murgatroyd after his father, you see.
Stephen because of his uncle, that's me.
His mother chose Monty, and she was emphatic;
While James, said his aunties, was aristocratic
So he was christened, but isn't it silly?
The only name anyone calls him is Billy.

Norman Hunter

Huffer and Cuffer

Huffer, a giant ungainly and gruff
encountered a giant called Cuffer.
said Cuffer to Huffer, I'M ROUGH AND I'M TOUGH,
said Huffer to Cuffer, I'M TOUGHER.

they shouted such insults as BOOB and BUFFOON
and OVERBLOWN BLOWHARD and BLIMP
and BLUSTERING BLUBBER and BLOATED
    BALLOON
and SHATTERBRAIN, SHORTY and SHRIMP.

then Huffer and Cuffer exchanged mighty blows,
they basted and battered and belted,
they chopped to the neck and they bopped in the nose
and they pounded and pummeled and pelted.

they pinched and they punched and they smacked
    and they whacked
and they rocked and they socked and they smashed.
and they rapped and they slapped and they
    throttled and thwacked
and they thumped and they bumped and they bashed.

they cudgeled each other on top of the head
with swipes of the awfulest sort.
and now they are no longer giants, instead
they both are exceedingly short.

Jack Prelutsky

Juniper Jim

Juniper Jim
Is very thin
As well as very old,
And if it wasn't for
The length of his beard
He would catch his death of cold.

John Jenkins

Mrs Golightly

Mrs Golightly's goloshes
   Are roomy and large;
Through water she slithers and sloshes,
   As safe as a barge.

When others at home must be stopping,
   To market she goes,
And returns later on with her shopping
   Tucked into her toes.

James Reeves

Be quiet

The world's greatest snorer
  Was Barrington Brown.
His snores shook the windows
  And rattled the town.

The people grew frantic
  And fearful with fright,
And cried to each other,
  'What happens tonight?'

They lullabyed softly
  But who could ignore
The deafening noise
  Of that terrible snore?

They tied up their heads
  And their eardrums they bound,
But nothing could soften
  That thundering sound.

They made a giant clothes-peg
  And placed on his nose.
With one mighty snore
  Like a rocket it rose.

So they all left the town
  In their cars and their carts,
'We must be away
  Before Barrington starts.'

Then Barrington woke,
  'Where's everyone gone?'
And then he turned over
  And went snoring on!

Max Fatchen

Pete, Pete

Pete, Pete, is always neat
From the top of his head to the soles of his feet;
He hasn't got any hair at all,
So he buffs his bonce like a billiard ball.

Anon

The sitter

Mrs McTwitter the baby-sitter,
I think she's a little bit crazy.
She thinks a baby-sitter's supposed
To sit upon the baby.

Shel Silverstein

The old maiden from Fife

There was an old maiden from Fife,
Who had never been kissed in her life;
Along came a cat,
And she said, 'I'll kiss that!'
But the cat answered, 'Not on your life!'

Anon

Fred

There was a pop singer called Fred
Who sang through the top of his head.
    It came as a blow
    When the notes were too low
So he sang through his toenails instead.

Max Fatchen

Hickenthrift and Hickenloop

Hickenthrift and Hickenloop
    Stood fourteen mountains high:
They'd wade the wind, they'd have to stoop
    To let the full moon by.

Their favourite sport, played on a court,
    Was called Kick Down the Castle:
They'd stamp their boots, those vast galoots,
    Till king lay low as vassal.

One day while spooning hot rock soup
    From a volcano crater,
Said Hickenthrift, 'Hey, Hickenloop,
    Who of us two is greater?'

Across the other's jagged brow
    Dark thunder seemed to drift,
And Hickenloop, with one swift swoop,
    Ate straight through Hickenthrift.

X. J. Kennedy

Lazy Lucy

Lazy Lucy
lay in bed.
Lazy Lucy's
mother said:
'You will drive
your mother crazy.
Upsy–daisy,
Lucy Lazy!'
To her mom
said Lazy Lucy,
'Little children
can't be choosy
(though I would
prefer to snooze
in my bed
if I could choose).
I will not
drive Mamma crazy,
I will not
at all be lazy,
I will jump
right out of bed
– and be Sleepy Lu
instead.'

N. M. Bodecker

I Like it When it's Mizzly

I like it when it's mizzly

I like it when it's mizzly
and just a little drizzly
so everything looks far away
and make–believe and frizzly.

I like it when it's foggy
and sounding very froggy.
I even like it when it rains
on streets and weepy windowpanes
and catkins in the poplar tree
and *me*.

Aileen Fisher

The dark gray clouds

The dark gray clouds,
the great gray clouds,
the black rolling clouds are elephants
going down to the sea for water.
They draw up the water in their trunks.
They march back again across the sky.
They spray the earth again with the water,
and men say it is raining.

Natalia M. Belting

Windscreen wipers

I sit in our car and to and fro,
In front of my nose, the wipers go.
To and fro, to and fro,
And wipe away the rain and snow.

Barbara Ireson

Thunder and lightning

About wind and rain,
I never complain,
But I wonder why thunder
And lightning's so frightening?

Barbara Ireson

Summer song

By the sand between my toes,
By the waves behind my ears,
By the sunburn on my nose,
By the little salty tears
That make rainbows in the sun
When I squeeze my eyes and run,
By the way the seagulls screech,
Guess where I am? *At the . . .!*
By the way the children shout
Guess what happened? *School is . . .!*
By the way I sing this song
Guess if summer lasts too long:
You must answer Right or . . .!

John Ciardi

Seasons

Spring is showery, flowery, bowery,
Summer: hoppy, croppy, poppy;
Autumn: wheezy, sneezy, freezy;
Winter: slippy, drippy, nippy.

To a red kite

Fling
yourself
upon the sky.

Take the string
you need.
Ride high

high
above the park.
Tug and buck
and lark
with the wind.

Touch a cloud,
red kite.
Follow the wild geese
in their flight.

Lilian Moore

Granny

Through every nook and every cranny
The wind blew in on poor old Granny,
Around her knees, into each ear
(And up her nose as well, I fear).

All through the night the wind grew worse,
It nearly made the vicar curse.
The top had fallen off the steeple
Just missing him (and other people).

It blew on man; it blew on beast.
It blew on nun; it blew on priest.
It blew the wig off Auntie Fanny –
But most of all, it blew on Granny.

Spike Milligan

The Britons of old

The Britons of old had a mode,
Of wearing smart costumes of woad –
  A kind of blue paint –
  They must have looked quaint,
I bet they looked cold when it snowed!

Langford Reed

Snowman

'Twas the first day of the springtime,
And the snowman stood alone
As the winter snows were melting,
And the pine trees seemed to groan,
'Ah, you poor sad smiling snowman,
You'll be melting by and by.'
Said the snowman, 'What a pity,
For I'd like to see July.
Yes, I'd like to see July, and please don't ask me why.
But I'd like to, yes I'd like to, oh I'd like to see July.'

Chirped a robin, just arriving,
'Seasons come and seasons go,
And the greatest ice must crumble
When it's flowers' time to grow.
And as one thing is beginning
So another thing must die,
And there's never been a snowman
Who has ever seen July.
No, they never see July, no matter how they try.
No, they never ever, never ever, never see July.'

But the snowman sniffed his carrot nose
And said, 'At least I'll try.'
And he bravely smiled his frosty smile
And blinked his coal-black eye.
And there he stood and faced the sun
A blazin' from the sky –
And I really cannot tell you
If he ever saw July.
Did he ever see July? You can guess as well as I
If he ever, if he never, if he ever saw July.

Shel Silverstein

Questions! Questions! Questions!

What do you know? It's going to snow.
How can you tell? By sniff and by smell.
What do you sniff? The wind off the cliff.
What do you smell? The ice in the well.
What do they say? It's coming this way.
How deep will it be? Two fathoms or three.
What shall I do? Stay here till it's through.
What shall I eat? Ox tail and pig's feet.
Where shall I sleep? In the pen with the sheep.
What if it gets colder? Put a lamb on your shoulder.
What if it melts? You can go somewhere else.
Then what will I get? Your feet good and wet.
How will I dry them? Bring them here and I'll fry them.
What of my dad? He'll say they taste bad.
What of my mother? She'll cuddle your brother.
What about you? I'll be glad when you're through.

John Ciardi

Footsteps

Our lawn, which yesterday was green,
Today is nowhere to be seen.
The snow fell heavily all night
Leaving a covering of white.
It's smooth as icing and as clean.
Nothing has spoiled it. No one's been.
But in a minute I shall go
In wellingtons across the snow
And every footstep that I take
Will spoil the icing on the cake

Barbara Ireson

Snowy morning

Wake
Gently this morning
to a different day.
Listen.

There is no bray
of buses,
no brake growls,
no siren howls and
no horns
blow.

There is only
the silence
of a city
hushed
by snow.

Lilian Moore

Shrieks at Midnight

Shrieks at midnight

I do like ogres –
There's something about them
So utterly ruthless
And yet absurd!
   I don't believe in them.
Yet I shiver
The very instant
I hear the word –
FE-FI-FO-FUM!

Dorothy Brown Thompson

Grim

Beside the blaze of forty fires
    Giant Grim doth sit,
Roasting a thick-wooled mountain sheep
    Upon an iron spit.
Above him wheels the winter sky,
    Beneath him, fathoms deep,
Lies hidden in the valley mists
    A village fast asleep –
Save for one restive hungry dog
    That, snuffing towards the height,
Smells Grim's broiled supper-meat, and spies
    His watch-fire twinkling bright.

Walter de la Mare

The Troll Bridge

This is the Bridge
of the
Terrible Troll.
No one goes
by
without paying
a toll,
a terrible toll
to the Troll.

It's no place to
loll, to
linger or
stroll,
to sing or to
play.

So if ever you
ride
to the
opposite side,
be ready to
pay
the terrible troll
I mean terrible toll
to the Terrible Toll –
I mean Troll.

Lilian Moore

51

A giant named Stanley

I ain't one to complain,
Don't get me wrong;
Something's been buggin' me
For far too long.
My mother's an angel,
My father – a saint!
And in all of these years,
I've but one complaint.
I love my mother,
My father I prize;
But why did they give
A kid of my size
      The gentle name of Stanley?
In the fabled days of yore,
Our tribe was famed for blood and gore:
      Cormoran and Blunderbore,
      Blunderbeard and Thunderoar,
      Gog, Magog, Asundertore!
      But not a single Stanley.
I'd have taken Blunderbore,
Shuttlecock or Battledore,
Close-your-mouth or Shut-the-door!
      Anything but Stanley!
      Oh, anything but Stanley!

Michael Patrick Hearn

Fear

From time to time I have to go
Close by a haunted house I know.
I never look behind for fear
Someone or something may appear.

Sometimes I have to take a street
Which echoes with my running feet,
I never look behind for fear
Someone or something may appear.

And if I have to cross the park
At midnight when it's very dark,
I never look behind for fear
Someone or something may appear.

A hooting owl gives me a fright
If I go home alone at night.
I never look behind for fear
Someone or something may appear.

I hurry under ancient trees
Where creatures rustle through the leaves.
I never look behind for fear
Someone or something may appear.

But next year I'll be eight and then
I'll go out in the dark and when
I'm all alone you'll hear me shout,
'I'm not afraid, so please come out!'

Barbara Ireson

Night sounds

Midnight's bell goes ting, ting, ting, ting, ting,
Then dogs do howl, and not a bird does sing
But the nightingale, and she cries twit, twit, twit;
Owls then on every bough do sit;
Ravens croak on chimneys' tops;
The cricket in the chamber hops;
The nibbling mouse is not asleep,
But he goes peep, peep, peep, peep, peep;
    And the cats cry mew, mew, mew,
    And still the cats cry mew, mew, mew.

Thomas Middleton

Running home

I look behind. Is someone there?
It's difficult to see.
The street is dark, I race along
And footsteps follow me.

Who's coming round the corner?
Who kicked that rolling can?
Who's hiding there behind the gate?
Who crouched behind that van?

The footsteps stop. I scan the street.
Someone's behind a tree.
Long shadows stretch across the ground,
Who's coming after me?

Barbara Ireson

The dog

I lie in bed and through the dark
I hear a dog begin to bark,
A sharp and urgent, fearsome sound
That fills the countryside around.
He's telling someone to beware.
What is it that he knows is there?

Barbara Ireson

Teeny tiny ghost

A teeny tiny ghost
no bigger than a mouse
at most,
lived in a great big house.

It's hard to haunt
a great big house
when you're a teeny tiny ghost
no bigger than a mouse,
at most.

He did what he could do.

So every dark and stormy night —
the kind that shakes a house with fright —
if you stood still and listened right,
you'd hear a
teeny
tiny
BOO!

Lilian Moore

55

Whose boo is whose?

Two ghosts I know once traded heads
And shrieked and shook their sheets to shreds –
'You're me!' yelled one, 'and me, I'm you!
Now who can boo the loudest boo?'

'Me!' cried the other, and for proof
He booed a boo that scared the roof
Right off our house. The TV set
Jumped higher than a jumbo jet.

The first ghost snickered. 'Why, you creep,
Call that a boo? That feeble beep?
Hear *this*!' – and sucking in a blast
Of wind, he puffed his sheet so vast

And booed so hard, a passing goose
Lost all its down. The moon shook loose
And fell and smashed to smithereens –
Stars scattered like spilled jellybeans.

'How's that for booing, boy? I win,'
Said one. The other scratched a chin
Where only bone was – 'Win or lose?
How can we tell whose boo is whose?'

X. J. Kennedy

Singing ghost

At the circus I was watching
Two dogs and a parakeet
When a ghost appeared before me
Dancing without any feet.
'Hey,' I said, 'what are you doing?'
He said, 'Giving you a treat.'
'Look,' I said, 'I'm at the circus.
Don't you know you can't compete?'
He said, 'No, my act's the greatest,'
And he burst into a song:
Oola oola woo balloola
Oola woola woola bong.
'Stop,' I said, 'I'll get in trouble,
You are being such a pest.'
In a moment cops appeared and
Threatened me with quick arrest.
'Come along with us,' they ordered,
'Songs that interrupt won't do.'
So they took me off to prison
And the singing ghost came too.

Steven Kroll

Who's scared now?

I'm warning you.
Don't scare me.
Don't go 'Boo'.
Will you?
Don't say you're from space
Or some awful place.
That you're a deep–sea creature
Or a late–night movie monster,
Will you?
Because –
ZAP!
POW!
I'm disintegrating you now.
Click,
Tick!
You are reassembled
And changed,
Your matter
Rearranged,
Thirteen million light years away,
If it's a day,
On the planet Zen,
With a scratchy pen,
Doing four million lines,
In the Homework Mines.
And it serves you right
For frightening me last night.

Max Fatchen

Sir Hector

Sir Hector was a spectre
And he loved a lady ghost;
At midnight he'd collect her
And he'd drive her to the coast.

And there upon the shingle
They would rattle all their bones,
And ocean sounds would mingle
With their melancholy moans.

Colin West

Fairy story

I went into the wood one day
And there I walked and lost my way

When it was so dark I could not see
A little creature came to me

He said if I would sing a song
The time would not be very long

But first I must let him hold my hand tight
Or else the wood would give me a fright

I sang a song, he let me go
But now I am home again there is nobody I know.

Stevie Smith

The games of night

When the ghost comes, I don't see her
I smell the licorice drops in her pocket.
I climb out of bed, I draw her bath.
She has come a long way, and I know she's tired.

By the light of the moon, the water splashes.
By the light of the stars, the soap leaps,
it dives, it pummels the air,
it scrubs off the dust of not–seeing.

and I see her sandals, black like mine,
and I see her dress, white like mine.
Little by little, she comes clear
She rises up in a skin of water

As long as the water shines, I can see her.
As long as I see her, we can play
by the light of the moon on my bed,
by the light of the stars on my bear
till the sun opens its eye, the sun that wakes things,
the sun that doesn't believe in ghosts . . .

Nancy Willard

The small ghostie

When it's late and it's dark
And everyone sleeps . . . shhh shhh shhh,
Into our kitchen
A small ghostie creeps . . . shhh shhh shhh.

We hear knockings and raps
And then rattles and taps,

Then he clatters and clangs
And he batters and bangs,

And he whistles and yowls
And he screeches and howls . . .

So we pull up our covers over our heads
And we block up our ears and WE STAY IN OUR BEDS.

Barbara Ireson

I never saw

I never saw
          a ghost on stilts
a witch wrapped up
          in patchwork quilts
a dragon
in a wagon
or a wizard wearing kilts.

I said
I never *did*.
I didn't say
I never *may*.

Lilian Moore

Fingummy . . .

Fingummy's fat
And Fingummy's small,
And Fingummy lives
With the boots in the hall.

If Fingummy bites,
If Fingummy tears,
If Fingummy chases you
Up the stairs
Shout 'Bumble-Bee Soup
And Bluebottle Jam',
And run up to bed as fast as you can!

'Cos Fingummy lives
Where there's never no light
And Fingummy makes
The dark sounds of the night,
And Fingummy's fat
And Fingummy's small
And Fingummy lives
In the dark, in the hall . . .   *Mike Harding*

What night would it be?

If the moon shines
On the black pines
And an owl flies
And a ghost cries
And the hairs rise
On the back
   on the back
      on the back of your neck –

If you look quick
At the moon-slick
On the black air
And what goes there
Rides a broom-stick
And if things pick
At the back
  at the back
    at the back of your neck –

Would you know then
By the small men
With the lit grins
And with no chins,
By the owl's *hoo*,
And the ghost's *boo*,
By the Tom Cat,
And the Black Bat
On the night air,
And the thing there,
By the thing,
  by the thing,
    by the dark thing there

(Yes, you do,
  yes, you do
    know the thing I mean)

That it's now,
  that it's now,
    that it's – Halloween!

John Ciardi

The witches' ride

Over the hills
Where the edge of the light
Deepens and darkens
To ebony night,
Narrow hats high
Above yellow bead eyes,
The tatter-haired witches
Ride through the skies.
Over the seas
Where the flat fishes sleep
Wrapped in the slap of the slippery deep,
Over the peaks
Where the black trees are bare,
Where boney birds quiver
They glide through the air.
Silently humming
A horrible tune,
They sweep through the stillness
To sit on the moon.

Karla Kuskin

Hallowe'en

Tonight is the night
When dead leaves fly
Like witches on switches
Across the sky,
When elf and sprite
Flit through the night
On a moony sheen.

Tonight is the night
When leaves make a sound
Like a gnome in his home
Under the ground,
When spooks and trolls
Creep out of holes
Mossy and green.

Tonight is the night
When pumpkins stare
Through sheaves and leaves
Everywhere,
When ghoul and ghost
And goblin host
Dance round their queen.
It's Hallowe'en!

Harry Behn

The witch's song

Hey! Cackle! Hey!
Let's have fun today.

All shoelaces will have knots.
No knots will untie.
Every glass of milk will spill.
Nothing wet will dry.
Every pencil point will break.
And everywhere in town
Peanut–buttered bread will drop
Upside down.

Hey! Hey! Hey!
Have a pleasant day.

Lilian Moore

Fat old witch

The strangest sight
I've ever seen
Was a fat old witch
In a flying machine.

The witch flew high,
The witch flew low,
The witch flew fast,
The witch flew slow,
The witch flew up,
The witch flew down,
She circled all
Around the town.
Then, turning left
And turning right,
She disappeared
Into the night.

That fat old witch
In a flying machine
Is the strangest sight
I've ever seen.
Of course it happened
On Hallowe'en.

Leland B. Jacobs

Bedtime story

'Tell me a story,'
Says Witch's Child,

'About the Beast
So fierce and wild.

About a Ghost
That shrieks and groans,

A Skeleton
That rattles bones,

About a Monster
Crawly-creepy.

Something nice
To make me sleepy.'

Lilian Moore

The witch's garden

In the witch's
garden
the gate is open
wide.

'Come inside,'
says the
witch.
'Dears,
come inside.

No flowers
in *my* garden,
nothing mint-y
nothing chive-y

Come inside,
come inside.
See my lovely
poison ivy.'

Lilian Moore

Frogday

I met a witch on Wednesday,
And Crabtree was her name;
I saw her next on Friday
And called her that again.
'Look here,' she said – her voice was bleak –
'We witches often change.
On Tuesdays I'm called Fenugreek,
On Thursdays simply Mange
And if on Mondays you should call,
You'll find my name is Lizard:
On Sundays I've no name at all,
On Saturdays I'm Wizard.
But Friday is a witch's own,
The witchiest day of all –
I'm Magpie and I'm Megaphone,
I'm Grimsdyke and I'm Gall;
And when I'm feeling really bad
I'm Bogey, Boot and Blog.
Now if you forget all that, my lad –
You'll turn into a frog!'

Shelagh McGee

Always Sprinkle Pepper in your Hair

Always sprinkle pepper

Always sprinkle pepper in your hair,
Always sprinkle pepper in your hair.
For then if you are kidnapped by a Wild Barbazzoop,
Who sells you to a Ragged Hag
Who wants you for her soup,
She'll pick you up and sniff you,
And then she'll sneeze 'Achooo,'
And say, 'My tot, you're much too hot,
I fear you'll never do.'
And with a shout she'll throw you out,
And you'll run away from there,
And soon you will be safe at home a–sittin' in your chair,
If you always, always, always,
Always, always, always, always,
Always, always, always, sprinkle pepper in your hair.

Shel Silverstein

Triolet

I wish I were a jelly fish
That cannot fall downstairs:
Of all the things I wish to wish
I wish I were a jelly fish
That hasn't any cares,
And doesn't even have to wish
'I wish I were a jelly fish
That cannot fall downstairs.'

G. K. Chesterton

Shopping list

I'm going on a shopping trip
For items that I'm short of.
Like lizards' legs and goose grease
And some other things I've thought of:
It's best to get them straightaway
Before the price goes up –
I must remember dragon's blood,
And oil of buttercup.
I'll need some wind for gas-bags.
Some wart-cream for my toad –
I'm out of stock of cochineal,
Perhaps I could use woad.
I want some jolly robins
To make a feather-brain:
I'd better wear my mackintosh.
My bunions forecast rain.
I'm going in a minute.
Just let me find a broom –
There's such a lot to carry –
Well, that cat won't have much room!

Shelagh McGee

Kangaroo – kangaroo!

The kangaroo of Australia
Lives on the burning plain,
He keeps on leaping in the air
'Cos it's hot when he lands again.

Spike Milligan

Oh, such silliness!

Oh, such silliness!
Silly willy-nilliness,
Dopey hillybilliness,
Rolling down the hilliness!

Oh, such craziness!
First of April Dayziness,
Giddy, goopy gayziness,
Bumpy dumb horseplayziness!

Oh, such sappiness!
Ridiculous slaphappiness,
Throw away his cappiness,
Jump into his lappiness!

Oh, such hilarity!
Falling down the stairity,
Tipping over chairity,
Shaving off your hairity!

Ghostliness and ghoulishness!
Push him in the poolishness,
Staying home from schoolishness –
Oh, such foolishness!

William Cole

Kangaroo shoe

A kangaroo
From Woolloomooloo
Found himself
A worn-out shoe.
He's getting tired
Hopping around
With one foot only
On the ground.
So if you see
This kangaroo
Please try to find
Another shoe.

Dorothy Barnham

Do you know the man?

Do you know the man with the flowers growing
Out of the top of his head?
Yellow flowers,
Purple flowers,
Orange, green, and red.
.Growing there
Just like hair
Out of the top of his head.
(Yes, you heard just what I said –
Out of the top of his head.)

Shel Silverstein

'Quack!' said the billy-goat

'Quack!' said the billy-goat,
'Oink!' said the hen.
'Miaow!' said the little chick
Running in the pen.

'Hobble-gobble!' said the dog.
'Cluck!' said the sow.
'Tu-whit tu-whoo!' the donkey said.
'Baa!' said the cow.

'Hee-haw!' the turkey cried.
The duck began to moo.
And all at once the sheep went
'Cock-a-doodle-doo!'

The owl coughed and cleared his throat
And he began to bleat.
'Bow-wow!' said the cock
Swimming in the leat.

'Cheep-cheep!' said the cat
As she began to fly.
'Farmer's been and laid an egg –
That's the reason why.'

Charles Causley

Granny's boot

Granny in her bed one night
Heard a little squeak!
And then a little
Peck-peck-peck
Like something with a beak
Then something that went Binkle-Bonk
Ickle-tickle-toot
And all of it was coming
From inside Grandma's boot!
Then the boot began to *hop*
It went into the hall
And then from deep inside the boot
Came a Tarzan call
The sound of roaring lions
The screech of a cockatoo
Today that boot is in a cage
Locked in the London Zoo.

Spike Milligan

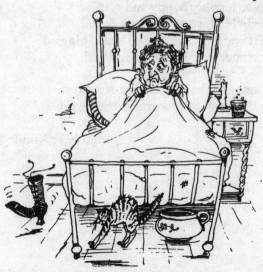

The longest tale about the longest tail

I am the longest, the longest, the strongest,
Yes, I am the longestest worm in the world.
I am so long, so far I extend,
That I haven't ever no never not ever
Oh, I've never ever seen my other end.

Well, I have been thinking and thinking and blinking
Yes, I have been thinking one very fine day
That I should flip, take a long trip
Until I meet it, oh meet it and greet it
Yes, until I meet with my opposite tip.

So there I was crawling and crawling and rolling
Yes, there I was crawling that very fine day
When suddenly there, just around the bend
I saw it, I know it, I know that I saw it
I saw it, I know it was my other end!

I was so happy, so happy and peppy
Yes, I was so terribly happy and glad
That I cried: 'Hail, you must be my tail!'
And then it wiggled and wriggled and giggled
And then it suddenly spoke up and said:

'I am the longest, the longest, the strongest,
Yes, I am the longestest worm in the world . . .'

Alexander Resnikoff

Multikertwigo

I saw the Multikertwigo
Standing on his head,
He was looking at me sideways
And this is what he said:
'Sniddle Iddle Ickle Thwack
Nicki–Nacki–Noo
Biddle–diddle Dicky–Dack
Tickle–tockle–too!'
None of this made sense to me,
Maybe it does to you.

Spike Milligan

Bad and good

Do you know what is bad?
I'll tell you what is bad:
To sprinkle catchup on your dad,
'Specially when he's mad.

Do you know what is good?
I'll tell you what is good:
To keep your foot out of your food
When mommy says you should.

Alexander Resnikoff

Bear in there

There's a Polar Bear
In our Frigidaire –
He likes it 'cause it's cold in there.
With his seat in the meat
And his face in the fish
And his big hairy paws
In the buttery dish,
He's nibbling the noodles,
He's munching the rice,
He's slurping the soda,
He's licking the ice.
And he lets out a roar
If you open the door.
And it gives me a scare
To know he's in there –
That Polary Bear
In our Fridgitydaire.

Shel Silverstein

The Ogglewop

The Ogglewop is tall and wide,
And though he looks quite passive,
He's crammed with boys and girls inside,
– That's why he is so massive!

Colin West

Mr 'Gator

Elevator operator
P. Cornelius Alligator,
when his passengers
were many,
never
ever
passed up
any:
when his passengers
were few
always managed
to make do.
When they told him:
'Mister 'Gator!
quickly
in your elevator
take us
to the nineteenth floor!'
they were never
seen no more.

N. M. Bodecker

Don't ever seize a weasel by the tail

You should never squeeze a weasel
for you might displease the weasel,
and don't ever seize a weasel by the tail.

Let his tail blow in the breeze
if you pull it, he will sneeze
for the weasel's constitution tends to be a little frail.

Yes, the weasel wheezes easily,
the weasel freezes easily,
the weasel's tan complexion rather suddenly turns pale.

So don't displease or tease a weasel,
squeeze or freeze or wheeze a weasel,
and don't ever seize a weasel by the tail, by the tail.

Jack Prelutsky

My Obnoxious Brother Bobby

My obnoxious brother Bobby

My obnoxious brother Bobby
Has a most revolting hobby;
There behind the garden wall is
Where he captures creepy-crawlies.

Grannies, aunts and baby cousins
Come to our house in their dozens,
But they disappear discreetly
When they see him smiling sweetly.

For they know, as he approaches,
In his pockets are cockroaches,
Spiders, centipedes and suchlike;
All of which they do not much like.

As they head towards the lobby,
Bidding fond farewells to Bobby,
How they wish he'd change his habits
And keep guinea pigs or rabbits.

But their wishes are quite futile,
For he thinks that bugs are cute. I'll
Finish now, but just remind you:
Bobby could be right behind you!

Colin West

It isn't

It isn't a bud
that turns into a rose,
but it grows.

It isn't a set
of musical bells,
but it yells.

It isn't a hippo
with triple chins,
but it grins.

It isn't a goat
eating paper bags,
but it na–aa–ags.

It isn't a vine
wrapped 'round a tree,
but it trails after me.

It's no other
than
my baby brother.

Eve Merriam

Brother

Why must we have him,
This new little brother?
He bawls all the time
And is really a bother.

He's not quiet like Teddy,
He does nothing but cry,
They say I must love him,
But I don't think I'll try.

He hasn't much hair
He's all wrinkled and red.
I'd much rather have
A new spaceman instead.

Yes, you may have him.
Please take him away . . .
But perhaps we should keep him
For just one more day.

Look how he laughs
When I stroke his small head.
I think that he knows
That it's me by his bed.

And, perhaps he would miss me,
I am his big brother.
There's just him and me
And our Daddy and Mother.

Barbara Ireson

Grandpa dropped his glasses

Grandpa dropped his glasses once
In a pot of dye,
And when he put them on again
He saw a purple sky.
Purple birds were rising up
From a purple hill,
Men were grinding purple cider
At a purple mill.
Purple Adeline was playing
With a purple doll,
Little purple dragon flies
Were crawling up the wall.
And at the supper-table
He got crazy as a loon
From eating purple apple dumplings
With a purple spoon.

Leroy F. Jackson

Babbling and gabbling

My Granny's an absolute corker,
My Granny's an absolute cracker,
But she's Britain's speediest talker
And champion yackety-yacker!

Everyone's fond of my Granny,
Everyone thinks she's nice,
But before you can say Jack Robinson,
My Granny's said it twice!

Kit Wright

My Granny is a witch

I'm a very small boy
and my Granny is a witch
I love my Granny very much
but she's a witch.
Once on a summer night
she got up and went into the kitchen
I crept after her
and there was a strong smell of onions
up hopped Granny on to the frying-pan
and burst out singing ever so loud
and I was ever so frightened
she beckoned to me
and together we flew out of the window
I held on as hard as I could
because the earth below was like a cup
peacocks were strutting over it
and swans swam all in white
it glittered like a Christmas tree
and we dropped into a cake shop
Granny stole some tarts
and I ate them
and Granny ate even more
because she was very tired
and then we came back on a pony
we got undressed ever so quietly
and slipped into bed
Granny told me not to make a noise.
Granny's very kind
it's a pity she's a witch though.

Arkady Mikhailov

Poor Gran

On this subject I'm sorry to speak
It happened on Saturday week.
    They loaded poor Gran
    In a furniture van
And auctioned her off as antique.   *Max Fatchen*

Jo

You say that Jo has made you late,
You say that Jo has dropped a plate.
You say he never leaves your side,
But when I'm here he seems to hide.
Sometimes I think he must be shy,
Or is it that he's very sly?
He breaks your toys, he picks my flowers,
He keeps you out for hours and hours.
Poor secret Jo, it seems a shame
He always has to take the blame.
I wonder is it really true
It's always him and never you?

Barbara Ireson

Did you?

Having little kids around, they say, is truly bliss;
But did you ever hear of any little kid like this?

He swallows pits,
Has temper fits,
Spills the ink,
And clogs the sink.
And, oh my gosh!
He hates to wash!
He plays with matches,
And grabs and snatches.
He scrawls on walls,
And sprawls and bawls,
And argues and fights,
And kicks and bites . . .
You say you never heard of
    any kid like that, you do—
Well, I know one who's
    just like that and it's
                        Y
                          O
                            U!

William Cole

Cousin Jane

Yesterday my cousin Jane
Said she was an aeroplane,
But I wanted further proof—
So I pushed her off the roof.

Colin West

Music makers

My Auntie plays the piccolo
My uncle plays the flute,
They practise every night at ten
Tweetly tweet *Toot-toot*!

My Granny plays the banjo,
My Grandad plays the drum,
They practise every night at nine
Plankety plank *Bumm-bumm*!!

My sister plays the tuba
My brother plays guitar,
They practise every night at six
Twankity *Oom-pa-pa*!!!

My mother plays the mouth organ,
My daddy plays oboe,
They practise every night at eight
Pompity-pom suck-blow!!!!

Anon

Billy Batter

Billy Batter,
What's the matter?
How come you're so sad?
    I lost my cat
    In the laundromat,
And a dragon ran off with my dad,
    My dad—
A dragon ran off with my dad!

Billy Batter,
What's the matter?
How come you're so glum?
    I ripped my jeans
    On the Coke machine,
And a monster ran off with my mum,
    My mum—
A monster ran off with my mum!

Billy Batter,
Now you're better—
Happy as a tack!
    The dragon's gone
    To Saskatchewan;
    The monster fell
    In a wishing-well;
    The cat showed up
    With a new-born pup;
    I fixed the rips
    With potato chips,
And my dad and my mum came back,
    Came back—
My dad and my mum came back!

Dennis Lee

Hugger mugger

I'd sooner be
Jumped and thumped and dumped,

I'd sooner be
Slugged and mugged . . . than *hugged* . . .

And clobbered with a slobbering
Kiss by my Auntie Jean:

You know what I mean:

Whenever she comes to stay,
You know you're bound

To get one.
A quick
  short
  peck
  would
  be
  O.K.
But this is a
Whacking great
Smacking great
Wet one!

Kit Wright

When

When I'm an aunt I shan't
Sip tea and criticise,
Won't buy my nieces socks,
Or my nephews ties.
For birthdays I'll send monkeys,
White mice and pirate suits;
At Christmas sets for chemistry,
And tambourines and flutes.
At Easter I'll bring chocolate eggs,
Not hymn books of white leather,
And I'll never scold at muddy feet
Or dogs in rainy weather.
When I'm an aunt I'll never mind
Rough ball games on my lawn,
And even turn an eye that's blind
To pillow fights at dawn.

Shelagh McGee

Toffee's Chewy

Toffee's chewy

Toffee's chewy,
Treacle's gooey,
Ice cream's licky,
Honey's sticky,
Nuts are crunchy,
Chocolate's munchy . . .

All these things
I love to eat
But POPCORN is
My favourite treat.

Barbara Ireson

Spaghetti

Spaghetti, spaghetti, all over the place,
Up to my elbows – up to my face,
Over the carpet and under the chairs,
Into the hammock and wound round the stairs,
Filling the bathtub and covering the desk,
Making the sofa a mad mushy mess.

The party is ruined, I'm terribly worried,
The guests have all left (unless they're all buried).
I told them, 'Bring presents.' I said, 'Throw confetti.'
I guess they heard wrong
'Cause they all threw spaghetti!

Shel Silverstein

The greedy giant

There once was a giant
So far from compliant,
    He wouldn't eat toast with his tea.
'A substance so horrid
Brings pains in my forehead,
    And aches in my toe-toes,' said he, said he,
    'And aches in my toe-toes,' said he.

They brought him a tartlet
To cheer up his heartlet,
    They brought him both jelly and jam;
But still while he gobbled,
He sighed and he sobbled,
    'You *don't* know how hungry I am, I am,
    You don't *know* how hungry I am!'

They brought him a cruller
To make him feel fuller,
    They brought him some pancakes beside,
They brought him a muffin,
On which he was stuffin',
    When all of a sudden he died, he died,
    When all of a sudden he died.

Laura E. Richards

Yellow butter

Yellow butter purple jelly red jam black bread

Spread it thick
Say it quick

Yellow butter purple jelly red jam black bread

Spread it thicker
Say it quicker

Yellow butter purple jelly red jam black bread

Now repeat it
While you eat it

Yellow butter purple jelly red jam black bread

Don't talk
With your mouth full!

Mary Ann Hoberman

The Mouse, the Frog, and the Little Red Hen

Once a Mouse, a Frog, and a Little Red Hen,
    Together kept a house;
The Frog was the laziest of frogs,
    And lazier still was the Mouse.

The work all fell on the Little Red Hen,
    Who had to get the wood,
And build the fires, and scrub, and cook,
    And sometimes hunt the food.

One day, as she went scratching round,
    She found a bag of rye;
Said she, 'Now who will make some bread?'
    Said the lazy Mouse, 'Not I.'

'Nor I,' croaked the Frog as he drowsed in the shade,
    Ren Hen made no reply,
But flew around with bowl and spoon,
    And mixed and stirred the rye.

'Who'll make the fire to bake the bread?'
    Said the Mouse again, 'Not I,'
And scarcely opening his sleepy eyes,
    Frog made the same reply.

The Little Red Hen said never a word,
    But a roaring fire she made;
And while the bread was baking brown,
    'Who'll set the table?' she said.

'Not I,' said the sleepy Frog with a yawn;
    'Nor I,' said the Mouse again.
So the table she set and the bread put on,
    'Who'll eat this bread?' said the Hen.

'I will!' cried the Frog. 'And I!' squeaked the Mouse,
    As near the table they drew;
'Oh no, you won't!' said the Little Red Hen.
    And away with the loaf she flew.

Anon

Chips

Out of the paper bag
Comes the hot breath of the chips
And I shall blow on them
To stop them burning my lips.

Before I leave the counter
The woman shakes
Raindrops of vinegar on them
And salty snowflakes.

Outside the frosty pavements
Are slippery as a slide
But the chips and I
are warm inside.

Stanley Cook

Rhinoceros stew

Rhinoceros stew
Tastes like glue,
While giraffe casserole
Sticks to the bowl.
An emu roast
Tastes like burnt toast,
While pelican fried
Turns the inside.
But none of this feed
Encourages greed.

Michael Dugan

Spaceman's complaint

It's very difficult for me,
When I'm in space, to eat my tea.
I float about, I have no weight
And keep on going past my plate.   *Barbara Ireson*

The sea-serpent

A sea-serpent saw a big tanker,
Bit a hole in her side and then sank her,
    It swallowed the crew
    In a minute or two,
And then picked its teeth with the anchor.

Anon

Sneaky Bill

I'm Sneaky Bill, I'm terrible mean and vicious,
I steal all the cashews from the mixed-nuts dishes;
I eat all the icing but I won't touch the cake,
And what you won't give me, I'll go ahead and take.
I gobble up the cherries from everyone's drinks,
And if there's sausages I grab a dozen links;
I take both drumsticks if there's turkey or chicken,
And the biggest strawberries are what I'm pickin';
I make sure I get the finest chop on the plate,
And I'll eat the portions of anyone who's late!

I'm always on the spot before the dinner bell –
I guess I'm pretty awful,
                          but
                             I
                               do
                                  eat
                                      well!

William Cole

When Betty eats spaghetti

When Betty eats spaghetti,
She slurps, she slurps, she slurps.
And when she's finished slurping,
She burps, she burps, she burps.

Colin West

Jelly Jake and Butter Bill

Jelly Jake and Butter Bill
One dark night when all was still
Pattered down the long, dark stair,
And no one saw the guilty pair;
Pushed aside the pantry-door
And there found everything galore –
Honey, raisins, orange-peel,
Cold chicken aplenty for a meal,
Gingerbread enough to fill
Two such boys as Jake and Bill.
Well, they ate and ate and ate,
Gobbled at an awful rate
Till I'm sure they soon weighed more
Than double what they did before.
And then, it's awful, still it's true,
The floor gave way and they went through.
Filled so full they couldn't fight,
Slowly they sank out of sight.
Father, Mother, Cousin Ann,
Cook and nurse and furnace man
Fished in forty-dozen ways
After them, for twenty days;
But not a soul has chanced to get
A glimpse or glimmer of them yet.
And I'm afraid we never will –
Poor Jelly Jake and Butter Bill.

Leroy F. Jackson

The lion

The lion just adores to eat
A lot of red and tender meat,
And if you ask the lion what
Is much the tenderest of the lot,
He will not say a roast of lamb
Or curried beef or devilled ham

Or crispy pork or corned-beef hash
Or sausages or mutton mash.
Then could it be a big plump hen?
He answers 'No'. What is it, then?
Oh, lion dear, could I not make
You happy with a lovely steak?

Could I entice you from your lair
With rabbit pie or roasted hare?
The lion smiled and shook his head.
He came up very close and said,
'The meat I am about to chew
Is neither steak nor chops. It's you.'

Roald Dahl

The sausage

The sausage is a cunning bird
With feathers long and wavy,
It swims about the frying pan
And makes its nest in gravy.

Anon

Old Joe Clarke

Old Joe Clarke, he had a house,
Was fifteen storeys high,
And every darn room in that house
Was full of chicken pie.

I went down to Old Joe Clarke's
And found him eating supper;
I stubbed my toe on the table leg
And stuck my nose in the butter.

I went down to Old Joe Clarke's
But Old Joe wasn't in;
I sat right down on the red–hot stove
And got right up again.

Old Joe Clarke had a candy box
To keep his sweetheart in;
He'd take her out and kiss her twice
And put her back again.

Anon

A man of the dunes

A delicious old man of the dunes
dined sweetly on beach plums and prunes,
and danced by the ocean
in lovely slow motion
while humming the yummiest tunes.

N. M. Bodecker

The boy stood in the supper-room

The boy stood in the supper-room
   Whence all but he had fled;
He'd eaten seven pots of jam
   And he was gorged with bread.

'Oh, one more crust before I bust!'
   He cried in accents wild;
He licked the plates, he sucked the spoons –
   He was a vulgar child.

There came a burst of thunder-sound –
   The boy – oh! where was he?
Ask of the maid who mopped him up,
   The bread crumbs and the tea!

Anon

I scream

Nicodemus Nicholas Belvedere Brown
is the very best ice cream eater in town.
A cone or a cup,
he'll guzzle it up;
a sundae with sprinkles
gives him the twinkles.
Strawberry, banana, vanilla macaroon,
he can eat ice cream from here to the moon.
He dreams of chocolate chip, dish after dish,
and pistachio's his favourite flavourful wish.
He can't get enough
of the meltaway lipadrip lap-and-lick stuff.
Rocky road marshmallow! Orange mandarin!
Ginger peachy! Pack it all in!

'No,' says his mother, 'just one portion.'
'Well, then,' says Nick, 'may I pick the dish?'
'I guess,' says his mother, 'I guess you may.'
Says Nick, 'Hooray.'
'Then the dish that I pick is rather small,
Just the size of a red bouncing ball
that expands to be as big as a bed,
a bed that's so high and so wide and so deep
that inside it ten fat men can sleep
and a horse and a sheep can fit into it too,
along with a dolphin and a kangaroo,
and ten tall ships and ten more again,
and a forest and a farm and a factory and a mill,
and an airplane hangar and the highest hill. . . .'

'Stop!' says his mother.
'As soon,' says Nicky, 'as I fill the dish.'
'And that will be all?' his mother says,
'just that one dish that is round as a ball?'
'Of course,' says Nick, 'for I don't want a portion
that's too big, I wouldn't like to be a pig.'

Eve Merriam

Giants' delight

Vats of soup
On table trays
Side of shark
With mayonnaise
Haunch of ox
With piles of mice
Mounds of gristle
Served on ice
Bone of mammoth
Head of boar
Whales and serpents
By the score
Tons of cole slaw
Stacks of rabbits
(Giants have such
Piggy habits)
Then, at last,
There comes a stew
Full of buffalo
And ewe
Followed by
Some chocolate cakes
Big enough
For stomachaches

Steven Kroll

I wish I was a little grub
With whiskers round my tummy
I'd climb into a honey pot
And make my tummy gummy.

Anon

The ghostly grocer of Grumble Grove

in Grumble Grove, near Howling Hop
there stands a nonexistent shop
within which sits, beside his stove
the ghostly grocer of Grumble Grove.

there on rows of spectral shelves
chickens serenade themselves,
sauces sing to salted butter,
onions weep and melons mutter,

cornflakes flutter, float on air
with loaves of bread that are not there.
thin spaghettis softly scream
and curdle quarts of quiet cream,

phantom figs and lettuce spectres
dance with cans of fragrant nectars,
sardines saunter down their aisle,
tomatoes march in single file,

a cauliflower poltergeist
juggles apples, thinly sliced,
a sausage skips on ghostly legs
as raisins romp with hard-boiled eggs.

as pea pods play with prickly pears,
the ghostly grocer sits and stares
and watches all within his trove,
that ghostly grocer of Grumble Grove.

Jack Prelutsky

Minnie

Minnie can't make her mind up,
Minnie can't make up her mind!
    They ask her at tea,
    'Well, what shall it be?'
    And Minnie says, 'Oh,
    Muffins, please! no,
    Sandwiches – yes,
    Please, egg-and-cress –
    I mean a jam one,
    Or is there a ham one,
Or is there another kind?
    Never mind!
        Cake
    Is what I will take,
The sort with the citron rind,
    Or p'r'aps the iced one –
    Or is there a spiced one,
Or is there the currant kind?'
    When tea is done
    She hasn't begun,
She's always the one behind,
Because she can't make her mind up,
Minnie *can't* make up her mind!

              Eleanor Farjeon

Snickles and Podes

Mean song

Snickles and podes,
Ribble and grodes:
That's what I wish you.

A nox in the groot,
A root in the stoot
And a gock in the forbeshaw, too.

Keep out of sight
For fear that I might
Glom you a gravely snave.

Don't show your face
Around any place
Or you'll get one flack snack in the bave.

Eve Merriam

Tea party

Mister Beedle Baddlebug,
Don't bandle up in your beedlebag
Or numble in your jimblejug,
Now eat your nummy tiffletag
Or I will never invite you
To tea again with me. Shoo!

Harry Behn

Piffing

Effily Offily
If If If
Niffily Noffily
Piff Piff Piff
I've Piffed at the Baker
I've Piffed at the Beak
Effily Offily
Squeak Squeak Squeak

Spike Milligan

Hitting

Use a log to hit a hog.
Use a twig to hit a pig.
Use a rake to hit a snake.
Use a swatter to hit an otter.
Use a ski to hit a bee.
And use a feather when you hit me.

Shel Silverstein

It was shut

'Sam, shut the shutter,' Mother Hyde
Called, her cap-strings all a-flutter.
'I've shut the shutter,' Sam replied;
'And I can't shut it any shutter.'

J. T. Greenleaf

Frying pan in the moving van

A new family's coming to live next door to me.
I looked in the moving van to see what I could see.
>   *What did you see?*
>   *Tell, tell, tell.*

Well,
I saw a frying pan in the moving van.
>   *What else did you see?*
>   *Tell, tell, tell.*

Well,
I saw a rocking chair and a stuffed teddy bear
and a frying pan in the moving van.
>   *What else did you see?*
>   *Tell, tell, tell.*

Well,
I saw a rug for the floor and a boat with an oar
and a rocking chair and a stuffed teddy bear
and a frying pan in the moving van.
>   *What else did you see?*
>   *Tell, tell, tell.*

Well, I saw a leather boot and a basket of fruit
and a rug for the floor and a boat with an oar
and a rocking chair and a stuffed teddy bear
and a frying pan in the moving van.
>   *What else did you see?*
>   *Tell, tell, tell.*

Well, I saw a TV set and a Ping-Pong net
and a leather boot and a basket of fruit
and a rug for the floor and a boat with an oar
and a rocking chair and a stuffed teddy bear
and a frying pan in the moving van.
>   *What else did you see?*
>   *Tell, tell, tell.*

Well, I saw a steamer trunk and a double-decker bunk
and a TV set and a Ping-Pong net
and a leather boot and a basket of fruit
and a rug for the floor and a boat with an oar
and a rocking chair and a stuffed teddy bear
and a frying pan in the moving van.
    What else did you see?
    Tell, tell, tell.

Well, I saw a lamp with a shade and a jug of lemonade
and a steamer trunk and a double-decker bunk
and a TV set and a Ping-Pong net
and a leather boot and a basket of fruit
and a rug for the floor and a boat with an oar
and a rocking chair and a stuffed teddy bear
and a frying pan in the moving van.
    What else did you see?
    Tell, tell, tell.

Well, since you ask it:
I saw a wicker basket
and a violin and a rolling pin and a vegetable bin
and a lamp with a shade and a jug of lemonade
   and a garden spade
and a steamer trunk and a double-decker bunk
   and a Chinese model junk
and a TV set and a Ping-Pong net
   and a framed silhouette
and a leather boot and a basket of fruit
   and a baseball suit
and a rug for the floor and a boat with an oar
   and a knob for a door
and a rocking chair and a stuffed teddy bear
   and plastic dinnerware
and an electric fan and a bent tin can
   and a frying pan and
THAT'S ALL I SAW IN THE MOVING VAN.

Eve Merriam

Circles

The things to draw with compasses
Are suns and moons and circleses
And rows of humptydumpasses
Or anything in circuses
Like hippopotamusseses
And hoops and camels' humpasses
And wheels on clownses busseses
And fat old elephumpasses.

Harry Behn

The cow

The cow mainly moos as she chooses to moo
and she chooses to moo as she chooses.

She furthermore chews as she chooses to chew
and she chooses to chew as she muses.

If she chooses to moo she may moo to amuse
or may moo just to moo as she chooses.

If she chooses to chew she may moo as she chews
or may chew just to chew as she muses.

Jack Prelutsky

Pop bottles pop–bottles

Pop bottles pop–bottles
   In pop shops
The pop–bottles Pop bottles
   Poor pop drops

When Pop drops pop–bottles
   Pop–bottles plop!
Pop–bottle–tops topple
   Pop mops slop!

Anon

The sniffle

In spite of her sniffle,
Isabel's chiffle.
Some girls with a sniffle
Would be weepy and tiffle;
They would look awful,
Like a rained-on waffle,
But Isabel's chiffle
In spite of her sniffle.
Her nose is more red
With a cold in her head,
But then, to be sure,
Her eyes are bluer.
Some girls with a snuffle,
Their tempers are uffle,
But when Isabel's snivelly
She's snivelly civilly,
And when she is snuffly
She's perfectly luffly.

Ogden Nash

Busy day

Pop in
pop out
pop over the road
pop out for a walk
pop in for a talk
pop down to the shop
can't stop
got to pop

got to pop?

116

pop where?
pop what?

well
I've got to
pop round
pop up
pop in to town
pop out and see
pop in for tea
pop down to the shop
can't stop
got to pop

got to pop?

pop where?
pop what?

well
I've got to
pop in
pop out
pop over the road
pop out for a walk
pop in for a talk. . . .

Michael Rosen

Smiling villain

Forth from his den to steal he stole,
His bags of chink he chunk,
And many a wicked smile he smole,
And many a wink he wunk.

Anon

The dripping tap

Drip drap
Goes the dripping tap,
Drip drap.

Flit flot
Into the old jampot,
Flit flot!

Plashes plishes
Over the unwashed dishes,
Plashes plishes!

Dillery dullery
All over the scullery,
Dillery dullery!

Tink tonk tank
On the draining-board plank,
Tink tonk tank!

Bink bankety bunk
On a pile of junk,
Bink bankety bunk!

Junk in the sink?
That's a bit odd, I think,
Junk in the sink!

But so is the pink
Of a dripping tap in the kitchen sink,
Pink! Pink! Pink!

James Kirkup

Who'd be a Juggler?

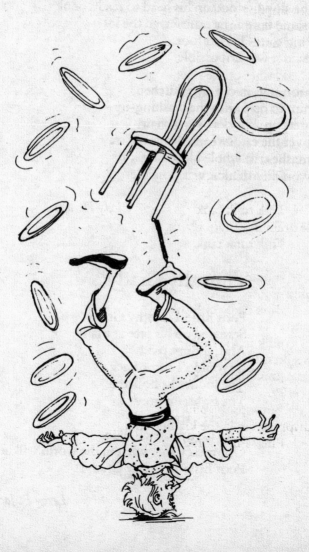

Who'd be a juggler?

Last night, in front of thousands of people,
he placed a pencil on his nose
and balanced a chair upright on it
while he spun a dozen plates behind his back.
Then he slowly stood on his head to read a book
at the same time as he transferred the lot
to the big toe of his left foot.
They said it was impossible.

This morning, in our own kitchen,
I ask him to help with the washing-up –
so he gets up, knocks over a chair,
trips over the cat, swears, drops the tray
and smashes the whole blooming lot!
You wouldn't think it was possible.

Cicely Herbert

Timothy Grady

Poor little Timothy Grady
Screwed up his face at a lady,
And, jiminy jack!
It wouldn't come back.
The louder he hollered
The tighter it grew,
His eyes are all red
And his lips are all blue.
Oh, mercy me, what in the world will he do?
Poor little Timothy Grady!

Leroy F. Jackson

Glasshouse Street

Don't throw stones in Glasshouse Street,
>In Glasshouse Street,
>In Glasshouse Street,
Don't throw stones in Glasshouse Street,
>Or you'll be – beat!

Two small boys in Glasshouse Street,
One March morning happened to meet –
>A stone flashed,
>A window smashed
>A chimney pot crashed,
>And the boys were thrashed!

So *don't* throw stones in Glasshouse Street,
>In Glasshouse Street,
>In Glasshouse Street,
Don't throw stones in Glasshouse Street,
>Whoever – you – meet!

Eleanor Farjeon

Clumsy Clarissa

Clarissa did the washing up:
She smashed a plate and chipped a cup,
And dropped a glass and cracked a mug,
Then pulled the handle off a jug.
She couldn't do much worse, you'd think,
But then she went and broke the sink.

Colin West

Polly Picklenose

'Polly, Polly, goodness gracious!
You just quit your making faces.'
Polly laughed at what they said,
Cocked her nose and went to bed.

But the big black Bugoo heard,
And he came without a word;
Walked right in – you bet a nickel!
In his hand a great green pickle;

Stalked along with steady pace,
Stuck it right in Polly's face,
Pinned it fast, and there it grows –
Poor Polly Picklenose!

Leroy F. Jackson

Accident

I took my girl to a ball one night
And sat her down to supper,
The table fell and she fell too,
And stuck her nose in the butter.

Scottish Children's Skipping Song

Tilda Tidbury

Tilda Tidbury
Went to school
With a nice clean face
And a cap of wool.
A skirt of yellow
And socks of blue.
A silver buckle
On each bright shoe.

Tilda Tidbury
Went to school
And saw a butterfly
Near a pool.
Its wings were silver
With dots of red;
It glittered and fluttered
Above her head.

Tilda Tidbury
Gave a jump
And down she came
With a great big thump!
Her shoes were muddy
And splashed her skirt;
Her little white cap
Was covered with dirt!

The silver butterfly
Flew right up,
Then lightly slid
To a buttercup.
There he turned to a queer little man,
Laughed ho! ho!
And off he ran.

L. H. Allen

Margaret Nash got wet but I don't know how

Margaret Nash
Went swimming – splash! –
Right in the middle of the Ocean.
'What? Swimming where?
Who took her there?'
– I haven't the slightest notion.

She jumped from a ship
And cut her lip
According to the Squid.
She fell from a plane
That was going to Spain
That's what Fish say she did.

She fell from a cloud
She wasn't allowed –
Except in dreams – to ride.
It changed to rain
And she couldn't remain.
Or so I'm told by the Tide.

She paddled on toast
Away from the coast
According to the Whale.
The toast soaked thin.
Margaret fell in.
– But what an unlikely tale!

What a pack of lies;
It's just not wise
To trust what you hear in the Ocean.
And truth to tell
The fact is – well,
I haven't the slightest notion.

John Ciardi

The wishing well

I climbed up on the wishing well
And looked right down.
Then in I fell!

The walls of the well
Are covered in slime.
They're much too slippery
For me to climb.

All I can do
Is holler and shout:
'I WISH that someone
Would get me out!'

Barbara Ireson

Help!

Catch hold of my leg!
Catch hold of my toe!
I'm flying away
And I don't want to go.

I bought this balloon
Just a minute ago
From the man with a beard
Who's still standing below.

Why didn't he tell me,
Why didn't he say
A balloon of this size
Would just fly me away?

Catch hold of my leg!
Catch hold of my toe!
I'm flying away
And I don't want to go.

Barbara Ireson

Hugh

There was a young fellow called Hugh
Who went to a neighbouring zoo.
    The lion opened wide
    And said, 'Come inside
And bring all your family too.'

Max Fatchen

Little Dimity

Poor little pigeon-toed Dimity Drew,
The more she ate, the smaller she grew.
When some people eat, they get taller and taller;
When Dimity ate, she got smaller and smaller.
She went for a walk, and all you could see
Was a tam-o'shanter the size of a pea,
An umbrella as big as the cross on a *t*,
And a wee pocketbook of butterfly blue.
She came to a crack one half an inch wide,
Tripped on a breadcrumb, fell inside,
And slowly disappeared from view.

William Jay Smith

Gobbling and squabbling

In a very old house
On a street full of cobbles,
Two very old ladies
Have got colly-wobbles,

And out on the pavement
The neighbours are grumbling,
And sighing, 'Oh *when* will
Their stomachs stop rumbling?'

Kit Wright

I used to have a little red alarm clock

I used to have a little red alarm clock.
It was my dad's.
He gave me it
and I used to keep it by the side of my bed.

It was very small and it had legs
only the legs were like little balls –
little metal balls,
and you could unscrew them
out of the bottom of that little red clock.

One morning
I was lying in bed
and I was fiddling with my clock
and I unscrewed one of those
little ball–leg things
and, do you know what I did?
I slipped it into my mouth – to suck
like a gob–stopper.

Well it was sitting there,
underneath my tongue
when I rolled over
and – ghulkh – I swallowed it:
the leg off my clock.
It had gone. It was inside me. A piece of metal.

I looked at the clock.
It was leaning over on its side.
I stood it up and of course it fell over.

So I got up,
went downstairs with it
and I was holding it out in front of me
and I walked in to the kitchen
and I said:
'Look, the clock. The leg. The leg. The clock – er . . .'

And my dad took it off me and he said,
'What's up, lad? Did you lose it?
Not to worry, it can't have gone far.
We'll find it,
and we can screw it back on here, look.'

'I swallowed it,' I said.

'You swallowed it? You swallowed it?
Are you mad? Are you stark staring mad?
You've ruined a perfectly good clock.
That was a good clock, that was. Idiot.
Now what's the use of a clock that won't stand up?'
He held it out in front of him,
and he stared at it. I looked at it too.
I was wondering what was happening to the leg.

Michael Rosen

Oh Erica, not again!

Every time we go on the pier,
  Or down to the sea, that is,
Erica says she is feeling queer
  And it makes her poor head whizz.

Erica says she likes the land,
  And there isn't, alas, much doubt,
As soon as she steps on a trippers' boat
  Erica's legs give out.

Erica's hands will clutch the rail.
  She hears the timbers creak.
She wonders where the lifebelts are –
  Or if we've sprung a leak.

There's never a sign of storm or gale
  But mother's crying 'Quick!'
And so it's just the same old tale,
  Erica's sick!

Max Fatchen

The fox rhyme

Aunt was on the garden seat
  Enjoying a wee nap and
Along came a fox! teeth
  Closed with a snap and
He's running to the woods with her
  A–dangle and a–flap and –
Run, uncle, run
  And see what has happened!

Ian Serraillier

This is a stick-up!

The world seems full of sticky,
It's everywhere I go,
Underneath the table,
And it's moving to and fro.

It follows me to school each day,
It gets into my books,
I swear that I don't put it there
But that's the way it looks.

I've got sticky on my fingers,
Sticky on my clothes,
Sticky inside my pockets,
Sticky up my nose.

My mother keeps on scrubbing
To wash the stick away,
The flannel just gets stuck to me,
My stick is here to stay!

She's hidden all the treacle
And all the sweets she can,
She's locked up all the Syrup
And every pot of Jam.

So *why* am I so sticky
And nicknamed Sticky Sam?
I really-*really* can't believe
How stuck up I am.

Spike Milligan

Time machine

If ever you should want to go
Into the future, let me know.
My new machine can carry you
Forward to 1992.

You'd really like to try today?
No time like now, I always say.
We'll get inside and shut the door,
I'll show you what the knobs are for.

Now please don't touch the one that's red.
Just use the blue and green instead.
The green one first and then the blue,
You'll soon see what you have to do.

You must have heard me when I said
That you must NEVER touch the red.
Oh dear! Oh dear! Look what you've done –
We're back in 1621.

Barbara Ireson

Adolphus Elfinstone

Adolphus Elfinstone of Nachez
Thought it fun to play with matches
Until the little Goop had learned
It hurt a lot when he got burned!
A *little* fire is queer and curious;
But soon it grows quite big and furious.

Gelett Burgess

Take Your Paws Off Me!

Take your paws off me!

Take your paws off me.
I really don't see
Why a tiger like you,
That lives at the zoo,
Should have my bun.
It's my only one,
Take your paws off me.

Barbara Ireson

The reason for the pelican

The reason for the pelican
Is difficult to see:
His beak is clearly larger
Than there's any need to be.

It's not to bail a boat with –
He doesn't own a boat.
Yet everywhere he takes himself
He has that beak to tote.

It's not to keep his wife in –
His wife has got one, too.
It's not a scoop for eating soup.
It's not an extra shoe.

It isn't quite for anything.
And yet you realise
It's really quite a splendid beak
In quite a splendid size.

John Ciardi

A house is a house for me

A hill is a house for an ant, an ant,
A hive is a house for a bee.
A hole is a house for a mole or a mouse
And a house is a house for me!

A web is a house for a spider,
A bird builds its house in a tree.
There is nothing so snug as a bug in a rug
And a house is a house for me!

Mosquitoes like mudholes or puddles.
Whales need an ocean or sea.
A fish or a snake may make do with a lake
But a house is a house for me.

A glove is a house for a hand, a hand.
A stocking's a house for a knee.
A shoe or a boot is a house for a foot
And a house is a house for me.

And once you get started in thinking this way
It seems that whatever you see
Is either a house or it lives in a house,
And a house is a house for me.

A flower's at home in a garden,
A donkey's at home in a stall.
Each creature that's known has a house of its own
And the earth is a house for us all.

Mary Ann Hoberman

Geraldine Giraffe

The
longest
ever
woolly
scarf
was
worn
by
Geraldine
Giraffe.
Around
her
neck
the
scarf
she
wound,
but
still
it
trailed
upon
the
ground.

Colin West

Odd

That's
odd
I must
say.

As I sat
on the
stump,
a piece of road
took
a lively
jump.

A small brown
clod
leaped
up
and away.

A piece of road!

Well, it *might*
have been
a tiny
toad.

Lilian Moore

The giraffe and the woman

Sing a song of laughter
    About the young giraffter
Who tried to reach the rafter
    To get the apple-pie;
The woman put it there, you know,
'Cause she was in despair, you know,
'He reaches everywhere, you know,
    And eats until I cry!'

Sing a song of laughter!
    The greedy young giraffter,
He got what he was after,
    And it was piping hot!
It burnt his mouth so terribly,
He yelped and yammered yerribly,
The woman chuckled merribly,
    And said, 'See what you got!'

Laura E. Richards

Hedgehog

He ambles along like a walking pin cushion,
Stops and curls up like a chestnut burr.
He's not worried because he's so little.
Nobody is going to slap him around.

Chu Chen Po
(translated by Kenneth Rexroth)

Two octopuses

Two octopuses got married
And walked down the aisle
Arm in arm in arm
Arm in arm in arm
Arm in arm in arm
Arm in arm in arm

Remy Charlip

Allie, call the birds in

Allie, call the birds in,
The birds from the sky.
Allie calls, Allie sings,
Down they all fly.
First there came
Two white doves,
Then a sparrow from his nest,
Then a clucking bantam hen,
Then a robin red-breast.

Allie, call the beasts in,
The beasts, every one.
Allie calls, Allie sings,
In they all run.
First there came
Two black lambs,
Then a grunting Berkshire sow,
Then a dog without a tail,
Then a red and white cow.

Allie, call the fish up,
The fish, from the stream.
Allie calls, Allie sings,
Up they all swim.
First there came
Two gold fish,
A minnow and a miller's thumb,
Then a pair of loving trout
Then the twisted eels come.

Allie, call the children,
Children from the green.
Allie calls, Allie sings,
Soon they run in.
First there came
Tom and Madge,
Kate and I, who'll not forget
How we played by the water's edge
Till the April sun set.

Robert Graves

Message from a caterpillar

Don't shake this
bough.
Don't try
to wake me
now.

In this cocoon
I've work to
do.
Inside this silk
I'm changing
things.

I'm worm–like now
but in this
dark
I'm growing
wings.

Lilian Moore

A big Brontosaurus

A big Brontosaurus lay counting
As he breathed from the top of his head –
He started at one,
And when he was done,
'I'm two hundred years old!' he said.

Barbara Ireson

So big!

The dinosaur, an ancient beast,
I'm told, was very large.
His eyes were big as billiard balls,
His stomach, a garage.
He had a huge and humping back,
A neck as long as Friday.
I'm glad he lived so long ago
And didn't live in my day!

Max Fatchen

The frog and the toad

Hopping frog, hop here and be seen,
I'll not pelt you with stick or stone:
Your cap is laced and your coat is green;
Good–bye, we'll let each other alone.

Plodding toad, plod here and be looked at,
You the finger of scorn is crooked at:
But though you're lumpish, you're harmless too;
You won't hurt me, and I won't hurt you.

Christina Rossetti

Hippos

Though hippos weigh at least a tonne,
They love to wade and wallow,
They never sink.
I sometimes think
A hippo must be hollow!

Doug Macleod

Hippopotamuses

Hippopotamuses never
Put on boots in rainy weather.
To slosh in mud up to their ears
Brings them great joy and merry tears.
Their pleasure lies in being messed up
They just won't play at being dressed up.
In fact a swamp is heaven plus
If you're a hippopotamus.

Arnold Spilka

At the zoo

First I saw the white bear, then I saw the black;
Then I saw the camel with a hump upon its back;
Then I saw the grey wolf, with mutton in his maw;
Then I saw the wombat waddle on the straw;
Then I saw the elephant a-waving of his trunk;
Then I saw the monkeys – mercy, how unpleasantly they
smelt!

William Makepeace Thackeray

The house mouse

Little brown house mouse, laugh and leap,
chitter and cheep while the cat's asleep,
chatter and call and slip through the wall,
trip through the kitchen, skip through the hall.

Little brown house mouse, don't be meek,
dance and squeak and prance and tweak.
There's cheese to take and plenty of cake
as long as you're gone when the cat's awake.

Jack Prelutsky

Mice

I think mice
Are rather nice.

Their tails are long,
Their faces small,
They haven't any
Chins at all.
Their ears are pink,
Their teeth are white,
They run about
The house at night.
They nibble things
They shouldn't touch,
And no one seems
To like them much.

But I think mice
Are nice.

Rose Fyleman

Glowworm

Never talk down to a glowworm —
Such as *What do you knowworm?*
How's it down belowworm?
Guess you're quite a slowworm.
No.   Just say
                    Hellowworm!

                         David McCord

Full of the moon

It's full of the moon
The dogs dance out
Through brush and bush and bramble.
They howl and yowl
And growl and prowl.
They amble, ramble, scramble.
They rush through brush.
They push through bush.
They yip and yap and hurr.
They lark around and bark around
With prickles in their fur.
They two–step in the meadow.
They polka on the lawn.
Tonight's the night
The dogs dance out
And chase their tails till dawn.

                         Karla Kuskin

The walrus

The widdly, waddly walrus
has flippery, floppery feet.
He dives in the ocean for dinner
and stands on his noggin to eat.

The wrinkly, crinkly walrus
swims with a debonair splash.
His elegant tusks are of ivory
and he wears a fine walrus moustache.

The thundery, blundery walrus
has a rubbery, blubbery hide.
He puffs up his neck when it's bedtime
and floats fast asleep on the tide.

Jack Prelutsky

Who's in?

'The door is shut fast
And everyone's out:'
But people don't know
What they're talking about!
Say the fly on the wall,
And the flame on the coals
And the dog on his rug,
And the mice in their holes,
And the kitten curled up,
And the spiders that spin –
'What, everyone's out?
Why, everyone's in.'

Elizabeth Fleming

The giggling gaggling gaggle of geese

The giggling gaggling gaggle of geese,
they keep all the cows and the chickens awake,
they giggle all night giving nobody peace.
The giggling gaggling gaggle of geese.

The giggling gaggling gaggle of geese,
they chased all the ducks and the swans from the lake.
Oh when will the pranks and the noise ever cease
of the giggling gaggling gaggle of geese!

The giggling gaggling gaggle of geese,
it seems there's no end to the mischief they make,
now they have stolen the sheep's woollen fleece.
The giggling gaggling gaggle of geese.

The giggling gaggling gaggle of geese,
they ate all the cake that the farmer's wife baked.
The mischievous geese are now smug and obese.
The giggling gaggling gaggle of geese.

The giggling gaggling gaggle of geese,
eating that cake was a dreadful mistake.
For when holiday comes they will make a fine feast.
The giggling gaggling gaggle of geese.

Jack Prelutsky

Worm

Worm
Is a term for a worm.
It sounds like a worm looks
Slow
Low to the ground
Usually brown
It would never have feathers
It would not sing at all
With a name like worm
It must be long and thin
And crawl.

Karla Kuskin

Worm

Little worm – wiggle wiggle,
You make me and my sister giggle.
You live in mud,
You live in wet,
You never ever see a vet,
You must be very healthy worm,
Wiggle Wiggle Wiggle Squirm.

Spike Milligan

The dog on the beach

As we sit on the beach,
Just preparing to eat,
A dog comes snuffing from group to group,
Shuddering a share of salt drops on each,
And flapping his damp tail;
He noses my spade and pail;
But when I reach to pat him –
(Brown eyes that beg,
And sea-wet coat all matted with sand) –
He makes one dart, and snatches the
Sandwich out of my hand!

John Walsh

A bumble-bee

What do I see?
A bumble-bee
Sit on a rose
And wink at me!

What do you mean
By 'hum, hum, hum'?
If you mean me,
I dare not come!

Anon

Index of titles

Index of first lines

152

Index of authors

Acknowledgements

The authors and publishers would like to thank the following people for giving permission to include in this anthology material which is their copyright. The publishers have made every effort to trace copyright holders. If we have inadvertently omitted to acknowledge anyone we should be grateful if this could be brought to our attention for correction at the first opportunity.

Joan Allen for 'Tilda Tilbury' from *Round about Eight* by L. H. Allen.

Atheneum Publishers for 'It isn't', 'I scream', and 'Frying pan in the moving van' from *A Word or Two with You* by Eve Merriam; for 'Mean song' from *There is No Rhyme for Silver* by Eve Merriam; for 'Snowy morning', 'The Troll Bridge', and 'To a red kite', from *Something New Begins* by Lilian Moore; and for 'Message from a caterpillar', 'Odd', 'I wish', 'Lost and found', 'The witch's garden', 'I never saw', 'Bedtime story', and 'The witch's song', from *See my Lovely Poison Ivy* by Lilian Moore.

Avon Books, The Hearst Corporation for 'Did you?' from *A Boy Named Mary Jane and Other Silly Verse* by William Cole.

Mrs Joyce Burnell for 'Kangaroo shoe' by Dorothy Barnham.

Jonathan Cape Limited for 'The lion' by Roald Dahl.

Carousel Books, Transworld Publishers Ltd for 'Windscreen wipers' from *A Bright Red Lorry*, 'Under my bed' and 'A big brontosaurus' from *Oh Dinosaur!*, and 'Spaceman's complaint' and 'Time machine' from *Spaceman, Spacemen*, all ©Copyright by Barbara Ireson.

Miss D. E. Collins and A. P. Watt & Son Ltd for 'Triolet' from *The Coloured Lands* by G. K. Chesterton.

Stanley Cook for 'Chips' from *Come Along: Poems for Younger Children* by Stanley Cook, published by the author, 600 Barnsley Road, Sheffield S5 6UA.

Curtis Brown Ltd for 'Hullabaloo' by Ursula Moray Williams, ©Copyright Ursula Moray Williams 1969. Reprinted by permission of Curtis Brown Ltd, London on behalf of Ursula Moray Williams.

Curtis Brown Ltd, New York for 'The Sniffle' from *Verses From 1929 On* by Ogden Nash, ©Copyright 1941 by The Curtis Publishing Company; and for 'Hickenthrift and Hickenloop' and 'Whose boo is whose' from *The Phantom Ice-cream Man* by X. J. Kennedy.

J. M. Dent & Sons Ltd for 'A man of the dunes' from *A Person from Britain* by N. M. Bodecker.

André Deutsch Ltd for 'Every few weeks someone looks at me. . . .' from *You Can't Catch Me!* by Michael Rosen; and 'I've had this shirt' from *Mind Your Own Business* by Michael Rosen.

Dodd, Mead and Co Inc for 'Advice to children' by Carolyn Wells from *Baubles*.

Faber and Faber Ltd for 'Lazy Lucy' and 'Mr 'Gator' from *Let's Marry Said the Cherry* by N. M. Bodecker.

Norma Farnes for 'Granny' from *Silly Verse for Kids* by Spike Milligan; for 'The Wiggley-Woggley Men' from *The Bedside Milligan* by Spike Milligan; for 'Kangaroo-kangaroo!', 'Granny's boot', and 'This is a stick-up!' from *Unspun Socks* by Spike Milligan; and for 'Multikertwigo', 'Worm', and 'Piffing' by Spike Milligan.

Elizabeth Fleming for 'Who's in?' by Elizabeth Fleming.

Robert Graves for 'Allie, call the birds in' by Robert Graves.

Greenwillow Books for 'The walrus', 'The cow', 'The house mouse', and 'The giggling, gaggling gaggle of geese' by Jack Prelutsky from *Zoo Doings*.

Harcourt, Brace Jovanovich, Inc for 'Tea party' from *Windy Morning* and 'Circles' and 'Hallowe'en' from *The Little Hill*, all by Harry Behn.

Harper & Row Inc for 'The sitter', 'Always sprinkle pepper in your hair' and 'Bear in there' from *A Light in the Attic* by Shel Silverstein; for 'Snowman' and 'Spaghetti' from *Where the Sidewalk Ends* by Shel Silverstein; for 'Do you know the man' by Shel Silverstein from *Oh, How Silly!*; and for 'Hitting' by Shel Silverstein; for 'Okay, everybody, listen to this' from *Near the Window Tree* by Karla Kuskin; for 'Full of the moon' and 'Tiptoe' from *In the Middle of the Trees* by Karla Kuskin; for 'The witches ride' from *The Rose on my Cake* by Karla Kuskin; and for 'Worm' by Karla Kuskin; for 'Engineers' by Jimmy Garthwaite from *Puddin' an' Pie*; for 'I like it when it's mizzly' from *I Like Weather* by Aileen Fisher; for 'What night would it be?' from *You Read to Me, I'll Read to You* by John Ciardi; for 'Oh, such silliness' by William Cole from *Oh, Such Foolishness*; and for 'Sneaky Bill' by William Cole from *Oh, That's Ridiculous!* by William Cole.

George Harrap Ltd and Little, Brown and Company for 'Every time I climb a tree' from *Every Time I Climb a Tree* by David McCord, ©Copyright 1952 by David McCord.

Cicely Herbert for 'Who'd be a juggler' by Cicely Herbert.

David Higham Associates Ltd for 'A kitten' from *Silver Sand and Snow* by Eleanor Farjeon; 'Minnie', 'Glasshouse Street' and 'Cottage' by Eleanor Farjeon; and 'Quack! said the Billy-Goat' from *Figgie Hobbin* by Charles Causley, published by Macmillan London.

Holiday House Inc for 'Singing Ghost' by Stephen Kroll; and for 'Giant's delight' by Steven Kroll and 'Shrieks at midnight' by Dorothy Brown, both from *Giant Poems*.

Holt, Rinehart & Winston Inc for 'The dark gray clouds' by Natalia M. Belting from *The Sun is a Golden Earring*.

Joan Langford Reed for 'The Britons of old' by Langford Reed.

Robson Books for 'Frogday' and 'Shopping list' from *Witches* by Shelagh McGee and for 'When' from *Smile Please* by Shelagh McGee.

Scholastic Inc for 'Teeny tiny ghost' by Lilian Moore, reprinted from *Spooky Rhymes and Riddles* by Lilian Moore, ©Copyright 1972 by Lilian Moore. Reprinted by permission of Scholastic Inc.

Ian Serraillier for 'The Fox Rhyme' ©Copyright 1950 Ian Serraillier.

The Society of Authors as the literary representative of the Estate of Rose Fyleman for 'Mice' by Rose Fyleman.

Nancy Willard and Rita Scott, Inc for 'The games of night' from *Ghost Poems* by Nancy Willard.

New Directions Publishing Corporation for 'Hedgehog' by Chu Chen Po, translated by Kenneth Rexroth, from *One Hundred More Poems from the Chinese*, ©Copyright 1970 by Kenneth Rexroth. Reprinted by permission of New Directions Publishing Corporation.

The Viking Press Inc for 'A house is a house for me' by Mary Ann Hoberman.

Mrs A. M. Walsh for 'Goldfish' and 'The dog on the beach' by John Walsh.

Other great reads *from* **Red Fox**

Further Red Fox titles that you might enjoy reading are listed on the following pages. They are available in bookshops or they can be ordered directly from us.

If you would like to order books, please send this form and the money due to:

ARROW BOOKS, BOOKSERVICE BY POST, PO BOX 29, DOUGLAS, ISLE OF MAN, BRITISH ISLES. Please enclose a cheque or postal order made out to Arrow Books Ltd for the amount due, plus 30p per book for postage and packing to a maximum of £3.00, both for orders within the UK. For customers outside the UK, please allow 35p per book.

NAME _____

ADDRESS _____

_____

Please print clearly.

Whilst every effort is made to keep prices low, it is sometimes necessary to increase cover prices at short notice. If you are ordering books by post, to save delay it is advisable to phone to confirm the correct price. The number to ring is THE SALES DEPARTMENT 071 (if outside London) 973 9700.

Other great reads ✎ *from* **Red Fox**

THE SNIFF STORIES   Ian Whybrow

Things just keep happening to Ben Moore. It's dead hard
avoiding disaster when you've got to keep your street cred with
your mates *and* cope with a family of oddballs at the same time.
There's his appalling 2½ year old sister, his scatty parents who
are into healthy eating and animal rights and, worse than all
of these, there's Sniff! If only Ben could just get on with his
scientific experiments and his attempt at a world beating
Swampbeast score . . . but there's no chance of that while chaos
is just around the corner.

ISBN 0 09 975040 6   £2.99

J.B. SUPERSLEUTH   Joan Davenport

James Bond is a small thirteen-year-old with spots and
spectacles. But with a name like that, how can he help being
a supersleuth?

It all started when James and 'Polly' (Paul) Perkins spotted
a teacher's stolen car. After that, more and more mysteries
needed solving. With the case of the Arabian prince, the
Murdered Model, the Bonfire Night Murder and the Lost
Umbrella, JB's reputation at Moorside Comprehensive soars.

But some of the cases aren't quite what they seem . . .

ISBN 0 09 971780 8   £2.99

Other great reads  *from* **Red Fox**

Discover the great animal stories of Colin Dann

JUST NUFFIN

The Summer holidays loomed ahead with nothing to look forward to except one dreary week in a caravan with only Mum and Dad for company. Roger was sure he'd be bored.

But then Dad finds Nuffin: an abandoned puppy who's more a bundle of skin and bones than a dog. Roger's holiday is transformed and he and Nuffin are inseparable. But Dad is adamant that Nuffin must find a new home. Is there *any* way Roger can persuade him to change his mind?

ISBN 0 09 966900 5   £2.99

KING OF THE VAGABONDS

'You're very young,' Sammy's mother said, *'so heed my advice. Don't go into Quartermile Field.'*

His mother and sister are happily domesticated but Sammy, the tabby cat, feels different. They are content with their lot, never wondering what lies beyond their immediate surroundings. But Sammy is burningly curious and his life seems full of mysteries. Who is his father? Where has he gone? And what is the mystery of Quartermile Field?

ISBN 0 09 957190 0   £2.99

Other great reads from **Red Fox**

School stories from Enid Blyton

THE NAUGHTIEST GIRL IN THE SCHOOL

'Mummy, if you send me away to school, I shall be so naughty there, they'll have to send me back home again,' said Elizabeth. And when her parents won't be budged, Elizabeth sets out to do just that—she stirs up trouble all around her and gets the name of the bold bad schoolgirl. She's sure she's longing to go home—but to her surprise there are some things she hadn't reckoned with. Like making friends . . .

ISBN 0 09 945500 5   £2.99

THE NAUGHTIEST GIRL IS A MONITOR

'Oh dear, I wish I wasn't a monitor! I wish I could go to a monitor for help! I can't even think what I ought to do!'

When Elizabeth Allen is chosen to be a monitor in her third term at Whyteleafe School, she tries to do her best. But somehow things go wrong and soon she is in just as much trouble as she was in her first term, when she was the naughtiest girl in the school!

ISBN 0 09 945490 4   £2.99

Other great reads ✎ *from **Red Fox***

The latest and funniest joke books are from Red Fox!

THE OZONE FRIENDLY JOKE BOOK
Kim Harris, Chris Langham, Robert Lee,
Richard Turner

What's green and highly dangerous?
How do you start a row between conservationists?
What's green and can't be rubbed out?

Green jokes for green people (non-greens will be pea-green when they see how hard you're laughing), bags and bags of them (biodegradable of course).

 All the jokes in this book are printed on environmentally friendly paper and every copy you buy will help GREENPEACE save our planet.

* David Bellamy with a machine gun.
* Pour oil on troubled waters.
* The Indelible hulk.

ISBN 0 09 973190 8 £1.99

THE HAUNTED HOUSE JOKE BOOK
John Hegarty

There are skeletons in the scullery . . .
Beasties in the bath . . .
There are spooks in the sitting room
And jokes to make you laugh . . .

Search your home and see if we are right. Then come back, sit down and shudder to the hauntingly funny and eerily rib-rattling jokes in this book.

ISBN 0 09 9621509 £1.99